SLIGO: Medical Care in the Past
1800-1965

This book is dedicated to my wife Mary

SLIGO
Medical Care in the Past
1800-1965

Dr. Patrick J. Henry

MARCH 1995

This Book was published with the support of the

NORTH WESTERN HEALTH BOARD.

All proceeds from the sale of this book will go to
THE NORTH WEST HOSPICE, SLIGO

I.S.B.N: 1 873437 09 9

COVER DESIGN: Patrick Henry

Typeset and designed by
Drumlin Publications, Nure, Manorhamilton, Co. Leitrim.
072-55237
PRINTED BY COLOUR BOOKS, DUBLIN.

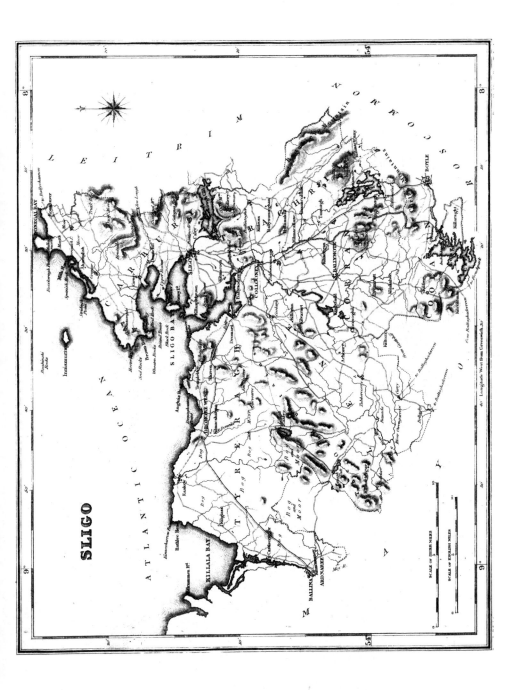

SLIGO

Acknowledgements

I wish to acknowledge the help I have received in compiling this record of past medical care in Sligo.

   Mr. John McTernan, former County Librarian, Sligo County Library.
   Mr Robert Mills, Librarian, The Royal College of Physicians, Dublin.
   Monsignor Dolan, St. Mary's Sligo, The Bishop's Library.
   Mr Brian Donnelly, National Archives, Bishop St., Dublin.
   Dr. Patrick Heraughty, Dublin and Sligo.
   Dr. John Fleetwood (Sr.) Blackrock, Dublin.
   Sir Peter Froggatt , Belfast.
   Ms. Una Lappin – Sligo

I also wish to thank Dr . Michael O'Connor, Dr. Sean Flannery, Mr Denis Boland, Prof. Stephen Doyle, Mr Seamus Mannion, Dr. Eileen Caulfield, Mr Willie Murphy, Mr Chris Higgins, Mr Pat Benson, Mr Peter Henry, Mr Aleck Crichton, Dr. Brian Gallagher, Dr. Tim Foley, Mrs Kilfeather, Dr. Harold Brenner, Dr. Ruairí Ó Bléine, MED. MEDIA, Dublin, Tommie Nairn, Fran Hegarty.

I thank my son -in-law Mike Kindle for time taken researching the Government Papers in the National Library and at Trinity College on my behalf.

I thank my son Patrick Henry who designed the cover for this book.

Photographs:
   Dr. Tom Murphy, Sligo Fever Hospital –
      (Courtesy Ms. Aideen Sweeney)
   Dr. Effingham Mac Dowel–
      (Courtesy of Mrs Deb. Perceval, Templehouse, Sligo)
   Dr. P.H.Quinn (Courtesy of Dr.Patrick Quinn, Wine St., Sligo)
   Dr. James Gordon Flannery –
      (Courtesy of Dr. Sean Flannery, Tubbercurry, Sligo)
   Photographs of the Old Infirmary, Fever Hospital, Asylum
      (Courtesy of Sligo Champion, Wine St., Sligo)
   Sketch: Sligo Fever Hospital – by Mr Derry O'Connell.
      (Courtesy of Sligo General Hospital)

I wish to thank particularly the North Western Health Board. This book was produced with their financial support.

Preface

This book is a record of medical care in Sligo between 1800 and 1965 and has been compiled from many sources. It deals with the major events relating to medical care spanning most of two centuries until just before the whole scene changed dramatically with the establishment of the North Western Health Board. This event greatly increased hospital manpower and the range of services.

A small publication in my possession by Dr Henry Irwin, Physician at Sligo Fever Hospital gives a great insight into the Cholera Epidemic of 1832 and is included in this book. It is important that the many doctors and nurses who gave their lives in that epidemic and in the later epidemic of 1849 are remembered. At that time the doctors of Sligo laboured heroically for their patients but their efforts were hampered by widespread suspicion and ignorance, ironically caused by their own earlier efforts to prevent the disease spreading to the town.

Kites were sent up to try and discover if Cholera had an atmospheric origin; well water was analysed and the people were advised how best to cope with the disease if it arrived. When the Cholera eventually struck many people blamed the doctors, believing that the disease had been brought down from the skies by the kites, or caused by poisoned wells or preventative drugs. These beliefs persisted in spite of the fact that five Sligo doctors died in that first epidemic.

William Middleton of Sligo, a man with extensive business interests was married to a Pollexfen. He died of Cholera shortly after assisting an unfortunate person who had collapsed in the street. After his death his widow sent for her cousin William Pollexfen to help her run the business. William Pollexfen was the grandfather of William Butler Yeats. Events have been recorded as accurately as possible.

The earliest Commercial Directory where the doctors of the

various towns are listed is 1820. The first Irish Medical Directory was produced by Henry Croly in 1843.

Great difficulty was experienced trying to obtain accurate manpower records. Some of the archival material rests in a warehouse belonging to the National Archives, somewhere in Dublin. Details relating to the recent past were often conflicting, on questioning my contemporaries. The Medical Council of Ireland had no records prior to 1927. Details of Medical Officers in Dispensary areas and Institutions were difficult to obtain. They are recorded on a manual register and are not recorded by county. The General Medical Council in England could not help. All records of doctors are maintained in strict alphabetical order, including the archival material from 1858.

The Armstrongs and the McMunns formed two notable medical dynasties in Sligo for much of the last century, as did the Flannerys the Morans and the Quinns in the recent past. It is interesting to note that because of the stability of the currency for over one hundred years medical and nursing salaries remained unchanged as illustrated in advertisements for jobs as late as 1920.

Another point of interest – with details of medical qualifications it can be seen that many of the doctors practising in Sligo in the early part of the last century qualified in Edinburgh and Glasgow.

Contents

CASTLE ST. SLIGO – *Sligo Abbey in the distance*

Introduction

As this book deals with Sligo in the past I felt it appropriate at the start to provide readers with a description of the town, first in the early part of the century and again in the latter part of the last century.

I personally believed that there existed a rudimentary town at that time, that medical services were scant and that doctors were few and far between. How wrong I was!

In the *Boundary Report of 1832* it showed that the population of the town had gone from 7,000 persons in 1800 to 15,151 persons in 1831. In the year 1830 – we are told that 540 vessels entered the port of Sligo. In the *House of Commons Inquiry on Emigration* during the Famine we find that among others many of the Lissadell tenants emigrated from Sligo Port. As a boy I well remember large corn boats from South America coming into Sligo Port on a regular basis.

Apart from the usual professionals such as doctors, architects and lawyers the town in 1820 boasted bakers, bleachers, linen dealers boat builders, book binders, boot and shoe makers, brewers, a coach maker, coopers, cutlers, a distillery, gun makers, hat makers, tanners and a tobacco manufacturer. (Commercial Directory 1820.)

Examination of the Government Papers relating to the *Poor Inquiry of 1835* was quite distressing. There was an Inquiry in each Dispensary area in the county. Several of the social conditions of the day, such as illegitimacy and poverty were examined, and the service that was being provided by the doctors to the destitute, was scrutinised.

Indirectly this Inquiry led to the enactment of the *Poor Relief Act of 1838* and the establishment of the Poor Law Unions. It depicted terrible poverty. People who had no ground, nothing but a hut in which to huddle together, with rags for clothes, were forced to beg if they could not get casual work. Their diet consisted of the potato which they shared with the less fortunate. Those who had plenty in many cases were indifferent to the plight of their fellow human beings.

Children supported their parents as best they could, when their parents were no longer able to work, which was as early as fifty years of age in some cases. Surprisingly no matter how little they had most were willing to part with some of their possessions for tobacco! The doctors in giving evidence commented that in many cases all that the sick poor needed was a simple plain meal.

When I was growing up, the doctor was seldom called. Even when I commenced practice in 1957 it was common to hear the expression "He was very bad, he had to get the doctor and the priest"! Because there was no information available one assumed that medical services in the town and county had been few and far between. Imagine my surprise to find that in 1820 there were thirteen doctors practising in Sligo town. In the *Poor Law Inquiry* of 1835 one learned that dispensaries in the main were supplied with medicines from pharmaceutical companies in Dublin. The doctors blamed most illness on the wretched poverty and a diet of only potato. Many of the patients were so deprived and starved that when they were given food their poor bodies could not tolerate it.

The salary of a doctor was a pittance and in the case of Dr Henry Irwin, who visited the Fever Hospital each day, his salary depended on the funds that were available. It is interesting to note that the subscribers of the Union had the authority to issue tickets to attend the Dispensary and could also direct the doctors to make house calls to the patients in their homes. The doctors themselves kept careful patient records, including a record of the medications that were prescribed .

I find it remarkable that there is no record, no monument, to any of the doctors or nurses who served Sligo so well in the past and how few persons had heard of Dr Henry Irwin or the five Sligo doctors who gave their lives for their patients in the Cholera Epidemic.

I understand that there were plaques in the old Infirmary honouring Surgeon Thomas Little and Dr. Effingham Carroll MacDowel. Were are they now? It is amazing that Dr Mac Dowel was surgeon to Sligo Infirmary for forty six years and scarcely anyone ever heard of him. The few that had heard of him said " There was a Dr. MacDowel and he lived on the Mall". It is a pity that they are all forgotten. It was pathetic to see how miserably they were treated. Dr. MacDowel was in his post for over forty years before his accommodation allowance was increased. Dr. Scott, dispensary doctor at Dromore West had barely enough clothes to cover himself or food to put on the table.

Dr. Petit, who was in charge of the Mental Asylum, seemed a very progressive individual, far ahead of his times in abolishing restraints on patients and allowing them the run of the hospitals grounds.

I do not think that the role of Irish nuns in education and nursing in this country has ever been fully appreciated. For this reason I found all the correspondence relating to nun nurses in the Bishop's library most enlightening. Submissions from Directors of workhouses all over the County were sent to the Bishop of Elphin, Dr. Clancy. Dr. Clancy was considering the introduction of nun nurses to the workhouses of the Diocese of Elphin: all without fail spoke of the wonderful dedication of those women. They provided excellent nursing care and ran the institutions efficiently. The poor patients no longer felt stigmatised after the arrival of the nuns. All the doctors commented on the kindness and care lavished by the nuns on the destitute poor.

Before they arrived, the records show the niggardly amount spent on clothing and food. In 1860 in the Sligo Union, out of a weekly cost per head of 2s.5$\frac{1}{2}$d only 5$\frac{3}{4}$ d was spent on clothing. In many cases more money was spent on postage, stationery and advertising than on medicine for the residents each year!

Likewise, in the *Fever Hospital Report of 1836* it was seen that because of the epidemic of Typhus involving four hundred

13

cases, expenditure was increased by £56-17s-8$^{1}/_{2}$d. Today Sligo has a state of the art hospital run by the most progressive Health Board in the country. When I started practice in Sligo in the late fifties the local health services were directed by a small group of dedicated persons.

This book should awaken Sligo people to the fact that as far back as 1800 Sligo was well catered for with doctors. It can be further seen in the *Poor Law Inquiry* that those doctors gave extraordinary care to their patients, having to be constantly available for very little remuneration.

It highlights the degree of deprivation that existed for the destitute poor, and the ill health that provision of simple food could in many cases have prevented.

Patrick J. Henry

March 1995.

INDEX

to the Map of the Town of

SLIGO

Published on the Scale of 500 or 10·56 Feet to One Statute Mile.

Scale of this Index–Six Inches to a Mile.

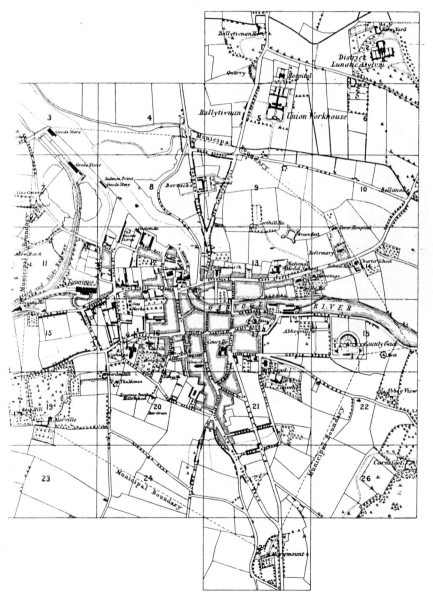

BOUNDARY COMMISSION MAP 1832

Chapter 1: Sligo in 19th Century.

A s this book deals with Sligo in the past a report on the town with a description of a proposed boundary change in 1832 is of interest.

1 The Town of Sligo is situated on the river Garavoge, near its confluence with the Sea, at the head of Sligo Bay. It is a place of considerable importance and a very rising Town, increasing both in Population and wealth.

The following Statements will give an idea of its comparative increase:

In the year 1800:	Population	-	-	7,000
	Vessels entered the Port			65
	Tonnage -	-		4,100
	Revenue of Customs & Excise			£6,120
1811:	Vessels -	-	-	100
	Tonnage -	-	-	6,879
	Revenue -	-	-	£10,715
1821:	Population	-	-	12,000
	Vessels -	-	-	275
	Tonnage -	-	-	19,666
	Revenue -	-	-	£29,754
1830	Vessels -	-	-	540
	Tonnage -	-	-	51,015
	Revenue -	-	-	£73,862
1831:	Population	-	-	15,151

There are a few Linen and stocking Weavers in the Town, who work on their own account, but not any large Manufactures. The depth of Water at the Quay is 12 feet, which will allow of vessels of 250 or 300 tons burthen to come alongside.

An Act of Parliament of 43 Geo. 3, gives certain Commissioners power to levy Harbour Dues, the Income arising from which is applied to the purpose of improving the navigation, making Quays, &c., so that the Harbour is improving yearly. The Exports of Corn, Butter and Salted Provisions are very large. Iron, Timber, Salt and every article of West India Produce is brought in, and distributed over a large tract of country, this being the only Port of any consequence for an immense extent of Coast, viz. from Londonderry to Galway. The amount of Custom Duties received at the Port of Sligo in 1831 was 30,987*l*, and the Tonnage belonging to Sligo and engaged in Foreign Trade in the same year, 3,284.

2. The Town is situated in two Parishes, (forming part of a union) viz. Calry and St. John's. There are, in addition to the above Parishes, two others in the union, viz. Killmaceown or Killmacowen, and Killaspickbrone. The Parish of Calry is on the North Bank of the River Garavoge, and St. John's on the South Bank; the latter contains the principal part of the Town, not only in Houses and Population, but the Markets, Quay, Warehouses, &c.

3. King James the First, in the 11th year of his Reign, granted a Charter to the Town of Sligo, created it a Borough, and incorporated the Inhabitants thereof under the name of the Provost, 12 Free Burgesses, and Commonalty.

   To the Provost and Free Burgess is given the power of sending two Members to sit in the Irish Parliament, but since the Union only one Representative has been sent to the Imperial Parliament.

4. The Freemen, of whom there are 15, compose the body called the Commonalty. The Charter states that *all* the Inhabitants shall be incorporated; but this privilege has fallen into disuse, and though a Mandamus was moved for in the Court of the King's Bench in Dublin, some few years ago, by an individual of the Town, by which he sought to obtain his freedom, it was refused.

5. The Provost is empowered by the Charter to hold a Court of Record, in which Actions of Debt can be brought which do not exceed the Sum of five Marks; no other Court can be held by him in right of his office.

6. There is not any Boundary to the Borough defined by the Charter. The Sligo Local Act passed in the year 1803, (43 Geo. 3,) states that the Precincts of the town shall extend one Mile Irish, from the Market Cross in every direction; this Boundary is stated to be for the purposes of the Act only, and not for any other purposes; but as it is a Limit of Taxation, and Persons living within it pay Rates to the Town, we consider that it ought also to be adopted for the purposes of the Reform Bill, though it will doubtless include a very considerable extent of Ground not occupied by Houses.

7. The number of houses and Stores of the value of 10*l* and upwards in the Town, is 603. The number actually valued at 10*l*., in the Cess Books, is only 532; but from inquiry we found that not only all those valued at 9*l*., but also a great proportion of those at 8*l*. were worth 10*l*., indeed paid 10*l*. 11*l*. and 12*l*. per Annum; we therefore have added all the 9*l*., and three-fourths of the 8*l*. Houses, and thus find the number of Houses probably worth 10*l*. per annum to 603; deducting from this number,

For Female Occupants	-	-	55	
Vacant Houses	-	-	33	
Double Occupants	-	-	5	(mostly Storehouses)
Disqualified Persons -	-	-	14	
		Total	152	

the remainder 451 will be the number of Qualified Occupiers of 10*l*.s Houses in the Town and Suburbs alone; to which we shall have to add those beyond the Town, but within the Limits of Taxation, if the later be adopted, as we propose they shall, for the purposes of the Reform Bill. The addition will be 45 occupiers of houses of the annual value of 10*l*. or more, and 15 occupiers of houses which are of that value including the land that is held with them, so that the total number of qualified occupiers of holdings within the circular Boundary, including Town and all, will be 511.

Of the present Voters there will be seven whose rights may be reserved, consequently the probable constituency under the Reform Bill will be 518.

8. The Assessments levied in the Town are the Lighting Cess and Church Rates; the former is levied under the Local Act above-mentioned, which empowers the Commissioners to levy any Rate not exceeding 2s. in the pound upon all persons living in houses of which the value is 5*l*. and upwards, or who occupy Garden of that yearly value, within the before mentioned distance of the market Cross; the Rate for the present Year is $2^1/_4$d. per pound on Houses of all values.

   The Church Rates are applotted on a valuation made of the Houses in the Town alone. The Rate for the Year 1831 is 1s. $0^1/_2$d. per pound on all Houses.

9. The Boundary which we propose to establish is, as we have already said, the Boundary defined in the Act for Local Legislation, 43 Geo. 3, c. 60, s. 17, viz. the space contained within a circle of an Irish Mile in radius, and of which the centre is the Market Cross."

[This Report was prepared in 1832 by T.C. Yates and

Thomas R. Mould.]

The town is again described in 1897 *'Ireland'* (M.J.B. *Braddeley)* and a small interesting map of the streets of the town and the outskirts is included:

Hotels:– Victoria (C.T.) in Albert Street, a little above the Upper Bridge (first class); Imperial, close by the Upper Bridge; both abt. $3/_4$ m. from station; buses.

Rail: to Enniskillen, $48^1/_2$m.; Dublin via Mullingar, 134m.

Cars to Ballina, 37m. twice a day, 5s; to Bundoran, 22m. 3s, and Ballyshannon, 26m., 3s. 6d. twice a day.

Private cars: About 10s., single; 20s. pair-horse, a day.

Post Office (Castle St.): – open, 7–8.45; Sun., 7–10. Chief Desp., abt. 2.30 and 8.15p.m. Del., 7 and 11.45a.m.

Tel Off: open 8–8; Sun, 9–10, 5–6.

Pop. (1891) 10,110.

Golf Course of 18 holes at Rosses, 5m. (car or steamer).

Sligo, the capital of the north-west of Ireland, rests its attractions on its surroundings, rather that on itself, though the slope on which a portion of the town is built, the towers and spires of its churches and public buildings, the bold clear-cut limestone heights which rise some distance from it, and the proximity of the sea, give it a picturesque and striking appearance when seen from any of the many elevations in the neighbourhood. The port is formed by the estuary of the river, three miles in length, which connects Lough Gill with the sea, and the best part of the town is on a level with the quay. The finest church is the R.C. Cathedral, on the way to the station–Romanesque in style, vast and imposing rather than graceful in appearance. The organ cost £1,500 and was in the Liverpool Exhibition. The chimes play a variety of tunes. Of the public buildings in the town, the Town hall, the Custom House, and the Court House – opposite the Victoria Hotel – are the chief. The streets, generally, though in no way remarkable, give evidence of a greater activity and prosperity than fall to the lot of most towns in the west of Ireland. The hotels are well placed near the river, the Victoria being a well-appointed house with English comfort.

In its surrounds Sligo offers a variety of excursions which may well detain the leisurely tourist. The drives round Lough Gill and Glencar; to Drumcliffe and Lissadell House; the circuit or ascent of Knocknarea, and a visit by land or water to the quaint little water-place called Rosse's Point, are all worthy of the time required for the excursions, but first we will describe the one attraction of Sligo itself.

To the tourist Lough Gill is the magnet of Sligo, and should on no account be omitted from his programme. The isolated hill of Knocknarea is also a very remunerative ascent.

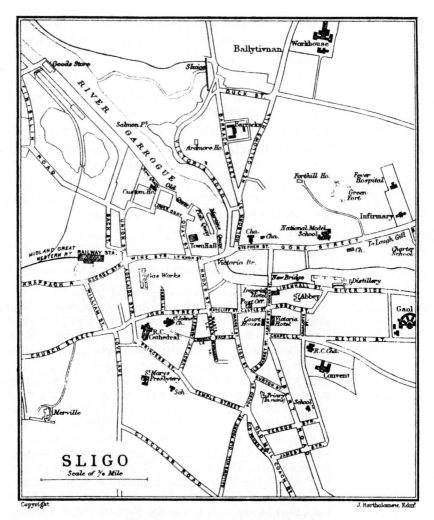

MAP OF SLIGO TOWN 1897

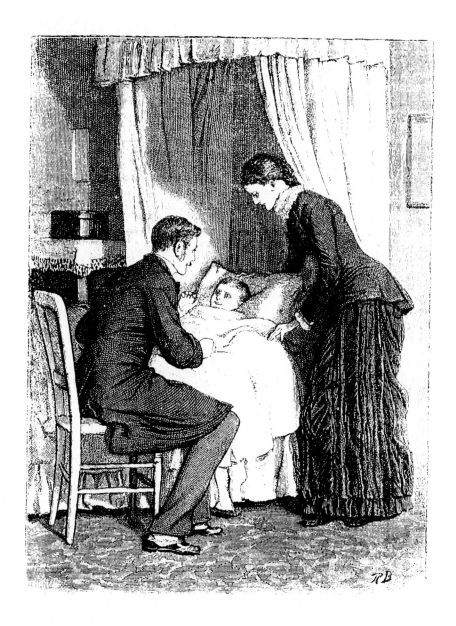

Chapter 2: Report of Commissioners relating to the Poor Law Inquiry in 1835.

This Inquiry was made in one parish in every Barony relative to different aspects relating to the conditions of the poorer class. A series of nine questions were asked about certain factors pertaining to the poor. Answers were also sought in 403 dispensaries, 56 Fever Hospitals and Infirmaries to thirteen questions. We are only concerned with examinations that took place in different parts of county Sligo. There were problems with the Inquiry.

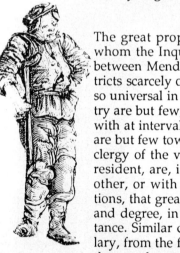

The great proportion of the Population about and amongst whom the Inquiry was to be made, is constantly fluctuating between Mendicancy and Independent Labour. In whole districts scarcely one of that class of substantial capitalist farmers so universal in England, can be found. The small resident gentry are but few, and the substantial tradesman is not to be met with at intervals of two or three miles as in England; for there are but few towns of sufficient trade to create such a class. The clergy of the various persuasions, and the proprietors, when resident, are, in many cases, so much at variance with each other, or with the working population, upon political questions, that great caution was requisite in regard to the manner and degree, in which we could avail ourselves of their assistance. Similar difficulties existed with regard to the constabulary, from the frequent collision in which they are placed with the people; and parochial authorities can scarcely be said to exist".

In the Inquiry relating to *Deserted and Orphaned Children* an examination held in Drumcliffe, Co. Sligo, for example gives some idea as to the extent of that Inquiry. The examination was held by James Osler Esq. and James O'Flynn Esq. and it gives us an insight as to the social conditions that pertained in Ireland in 1835.

Persons who attended the Examination at Drumcliffe

REV EDWARD ALWARD, protestant curate – MR. JAMES BARBER, land agent. – DR. COULTER, dispensary surgeon – JOHN FENNY, labourer – MICHAEL FENNY, labourer – WILLIAM P. FENNY, farmer – MR. P.McTUCKER, farmer – JAMES MULLEN, labourer – REV. MICHAEL O'CALLAGHAN, p.p. – REV. MR SAUNDERSON, presbyterian minister. – C. SYMPSON, farmer.

There is not a single deserted child in the parish; there are many orphans, but they are all supported by their relations. There have been only two cases of deserted children within the last five years; and since the closing of the Foundling-hospital in Dublin, the practice of desertion has been on the decrease. No further legislative interference is deemed necessary for the protection of deserted children, as a certainty of support would increase the number.

Report of the Poor Inquiry of 1835

Concerning *Bastardy* – Examination in different parishes are included and have a lot in common.

Drumcliffe (Sligo)

There are very few bastards, and these supported by the parish. The mothers seldom desert their illegitimate children and there has not been a case of infanticide more than twice these 18 years. The fathers are often induced to marry the mothers, from the fear of the woman's friends, as well of feelings of honour.

If the woman can prove a promise and part payment, she can recover wages at the sessions as a simple debt.

The people have a great dislike to marry a woman who has had an illegitimate child, and many more of them remain unmarried through life than are married. They frequently leave the country, and are sent away by their parents, as they consider it better to send them where they are not known than give them to inferior persons at home; they sometimes get husbands through the influence of persons in a higher station. At first there is great outcry against a girl who has a bastard, but if well conducted it soon wears off, and she is treated as usual, except when quarrels arise, and then they always charge her with her shame. There is also a strong objection amongst the farmers to connect themselves with illegitimate children and they will not give their daughters in marriage to them, without strong motives to counterbalance the disgrace.

Sligo Town

Persons who attended the Examination

REV. M.ARMSTRONG.– Right REV. DR. BURKE, roman catholic Bishop of Elphin.– REV. J. DUNLEVIE, parish priest.– R. FENNERY, labourer, –JOHN HARTE, shopkeeper. – FRANK KENNIT, labourer. JAMES KENNY, ESQ. M.D. dispensary. – JOHN MARTIN, ESQ., M.P – JAMES RAFFERTY, labourer. – WILLIAM STOPFORD, farmer.

The number of bastards in the parish in not known, but is supposed to be very small; they are never supported by the parish; are very seldom deserted by mothers; and cases of infanticide are never heard of.

Wages are never awarded to the mother, except she can prove a promise on the part of the father and part payment, she then recovers the support of the child as servant's wages.

Girls who have had illegitimate children find great difficulty in procuring husbands; no man who knows of her 'misfortune' will marry her, unless induced by a good sum of money. Individuals of the poorer classes are often induced by persons of higher station to marry those women. It is the usual way of getting rid of them: a man who so marries is considered a 'mean fellow'.

Those women, who have had illegitimate children are looked upon by the rest of their sex in th parish with great contempt at first, but that wears off. William Stopford said, 'In some time she hears no more about it, until they quarrel, and then it is time to be the first thing thrown at her'. A good deal of this feeling also goes with the child; 'bastard' is a term of contempt, and a small farmer would certainly have an objection to give his daughter to a bastard, though otherwise an eligible match. It frequently happens that women threaten to swear a rape against a man, to force him to marry her; it mostly ends in marriage; they are often married in the dock during the trial.

Tubbercurry

There is only one deserted child in the parish: it is supposed to be illegitimate, and is supported by the parish. Marriages often take place through a feeling of duty on the part of the fathers of illegitimate children strengthened by the influence of the clergy.

'Girls who have had illegitimate children seldom get married except under peculiar circumstances, especially the possession of a little money or a cow, as sometimes happens with the daughter of a small farmer. Women of her own degree will work with her after a bit, but they always look down upon her, and she is pretty sure to be reminded of what has happened if ever she ventures to quarrel with any body. Farmers would not like to give their daughter as a wife to a bastard, but they would allow it if the young man had a little money, or could get a few acres of land.' – (*Hugh Gray, farmer*)

W. Jones esq. J.P. says, 'The declaration of the woman must be corroborated by some acknowledgement, part payment, or promise of payment on the part of the reputed father; but we never decide these questions, leaving them always to the assistant barrister, who, on being satisfied with the evidence, generally awards 5*l.* to be paid by small instalments.

Report of the Poor Inquiry of 1835

Vagrancy: **In the Examination in Achonry Parish in the county of Sligo in 1835.**

Concerning the possibility of proposed tax to relieve the destitute, a farmer, by the name of Hugh Gray, gave evidence *"the farmers would prefer the present method of relieving the poor to paying a tax, as they do not feel what they give now, and always have a potato to give to the beggar, and may not have money to pay the tax gatherer. They are burdened enough already and would not consent to any compulsory assessment"*. However a weaver, John Robinson stated that many would go into a House of Industry if it was established, every man willing to work would go if his liberty was not too restricted. In fact he would readily go himself.

In a separate examination in Ballymote which was attended by Dr. Lougheed (sometimes Longheed), dispensary surgeon, the position was summed up by Charles Miland concerning the great increase in the number of beggars. *"There is a class of men who have no ground, nothing but a hut, in which they huddle together and depend entirely on day labour; this they cannot get of late and therefore have no other dependence but begging. Many also have three or four acres of ground which will give them potatoes alone for not more than seven or eight months, for part of the rent of this land and for support during the remainder of the year they must depend on work and when they cannot get it their families must beg. The farmers are now not able to employ them. Vagrancy is most common during the months of June and July owing to the scarcity of food and employment".*

H. McDonagh giving evidence stated *"the man takes his spade and the woman a bag and they go along the road. If he can get employment he will work, if not, his wife goes up to the farmer's house to beg while he loiters behind on the road".*

Mr. J. Garret stated that men who had been turned out of their land planted a 'spot' of con-acre. Since the decline of the Linen trade they were the most wretched part of the community because they were unable "to earn at their trade 3s a week" and were unable to work hard at outdoor labour. The Rev. B. O'Kean stated that *"scarcely any adopt a life of begging through idleness. The beggars get no meal, the people have no meal themselves, it must go to the rent. When they obtain more food than they require for their own consumption – they sell a little to buy tobacco which is considered an absolute necessity, but they can sell very little as they must keep some for a bad day when they cannot go out to beg".*

Some of the farmers were reluctant to tell what they gave lest it serve as a guide for which to tax them for a poor law!

The majority of beggars were driven to beg by absolute necessity. The most industrious were the most wretched because 5d or 6d a day could not support a family of five or six children.

"Relief is given to beggars for 'God's sake, and to keep them from starving', and never because it is the custom to do so; nor is it ever exhorted by mere importunity, for 'when refused they go quietly away.' Religious feeling would never cause a man to give to a beggar whom he thought was not in want; the farmers say, 'if we considered him not in want we would keep it for the man we knew was so' and charity is never given through fear of violence to the donor's person or property charity is not given through fear of the beggar's curse, who very seldom resort to such means of exhorting relief. The people said, 'we would not like to have the beggars curse, but would not give them anything to avoid it;' and Rev. Mr O'Kean said, 'they seldom curse in that way, and if they did there certainly would be a prejudice against such persons.'

There is no House of Industry or mendicity nearer than the town of Sligo. Some of those who beg would be willing to go into such a house, if established in the parish, but the great majority would be most unwilling to do so, so much so that Mr.Cogan said, 'you would have the house full of beggars here today, but that a report was spread that they would be all put into a house, and kept from roving about the county;' and John Davey said, 'when I was coming into town just now, I met many of them running away, lest they should be taken up'."

Report of Poor Inquiry: Sligo Town

In the town there are more than 100 beggars estimating by the applications for admittance into the Mendicity; it could not maintain more. In the country 50 families are frequently seen begging in one day.

Vagrancy is increasing as there is less employed, because in the country the farmers cannot afford to employ any one from want of capital, and will over-work themselves to avoid it. In the town there is less employment, because there is a stagnation of trade. The periods at which vagrancy are most common are July and August, because these being the dead season of the year, many strangers come in who are the wives and children of labourers who have gone to England or Scotland to seek for work. The town beggars are natives, but in the country they are strangers, as they are ashamed to beg in their neighbourhood. It is common for people in the town to go four or five miles into the country to beg, and they are principally composed of old and infirm men, women and children of every age; 'but able-bodied men, ' Mr. Martin J.P. says, 'very seldom beg'.

'I knew instances of the father's having given up his lands to his son, who then refused to support him, though able, but through my influence did so. Poverty has always something to do with the refusal, and there are thousands who would share their last potato with their parents rather than let them have the name of beggars'. The regular beggars belong to the towns; such are very seldom met with in the country; the strangers all belong to the country; there are but few vagrants children of beggars; some may, but they are by no means numerous, as grown-up children are scarcely ever sent to beg. 'I never', said Mr. Martin, M.P., 'saw a child able to work with a beggar; at

Gallows Hill with Dominican Friary in the background. Note: young girl with bandage.

some seasons 500 children may be seen gathering shell fish to sell or live on'.

Very little is to be obtained by beggars in town from passengers in coaches, cars, &c.; very little too can be had on Sundays at the chapel or church doors, as, since the establishment of the Mendicity, beggars have been prevented from begging at such places. Should a family of beggars, consisting of father, mother and three or four children, apply for relief, the quantity of food given would be increased but not in proportion to the number of applicants.

The men mostly beg under the plea that they cannot get work, or are ill, or otherwise disabled. The women say, their husbands are dead, or away at work in a distant part of the country, or in England. Rags, dirt, and such appearances, are not fostered for the purpose of exciting pity; 'it is not at all necessary, their own appearance bespeaks their misery'. Vagrants of that class called fair beggars, who attend fairs and such places, are supposed to exhibit at times pretended sores, but not to produce them in reality. A farmer said, 'there is too much of that; every man that has a sore shows it'. A man was tried some time since at the Session of Sligo, for exhibiting a pretended sore; but Rev. Mr. Armstrong said, 'it is not near so common now as formerly it was'. Beggars have not been known to refuse to have their sores cured, but have frequently refused to go into hospital, not lest they may lose the advantage of exhibiting them, but because they are afraid of their limbs being amputated.

These exhibitions of their sores are sometimes at fairs very disgusting, but not frequently now, as the police prevent them.

The beggars often share with each other. One man said, 'I am sure they do; they are more disposed to feel for poverty than other classes'. Rev. Mr Dunlevie did not recollect instances of beggars hoarding up money, but two instances were mentioned one of a man called 'Blind Cavaugh,' who, about two years ago, gave a woman ten sovereigns to live with him as his wife. Having lost his sight, he has no resource but begging, and seldom leaves the immediate neighbourhood of the town.

Another well-known mendicant, with a wooden leg, who begs constantly on Ballinode Hill (within half a mile of the town), not long since gave his daughter, on her marriage, two cows and two acres of land, and to his son, on the same occasion, one cow and one acre of land: his wife lives with him, and he has been a confirmed beggar for many years.

With regard to borrowing children for the purpose of begging, it was said that there is no certainty upon it; but it is supposed, that when two women have each two children, one will go out one day with the four, and the other the next.

Beggars have in general four or five children each with them, but they are never beggars when married; they never begin housekeeping with the prospect of begging; they think that when married they will be well off. The number of illegitimate children is very small. Rev. Mr. Dunlevie says, 'it is very small in any class'.

Cases are not now known; but Dr. Kenney says, 'I know that lives are very often shortened, by the insufficiency and bad quality of their food and hardships. In 1822, I often attended people who were *so weak from abstinence, that when food was given, it was more an injury than otherwise , as their stomachs could not bear it'*.

Diseases are often spread through the country by the custom of giving lodging to beggars; the Cholera was almost invariably introduced by beggars.

There is a Mendicity Institution, in the town but not sufficiently extensive; its annual income during the late two years did not amount to £250 collected chiefly by charity sermons at the places of worship of all denominations. The number of persons relieved by it at present is 51, 30 of whom go begging in the house. There is an unwillingness to go into this establishment, but it may be owing to the way in which the inmates are supported; they get each three pounds and a half of potatoes twice in the day, and half a pint of buttermilk at each meal. Dr Kenny did not consider this sufficient. On Saturdays they get a breakfast of 'stirabout' and at times soup or meat when any may be sent in by the market jury. They are all infirm men and women, and are able to do very little work of any kind; some few of the women spin, and are allowed to have what they can earn to buy tobacco and snuff; but the men are all so infirm that when a short time since the committee had contracted for sweeping the streets, they were obliged to hire four men to do it. The clerk of the house said, there is a reluctance to go in, they prefer stout begging, but if punished for it many would crowd into the establishment; some who were reluctant to enter became well content with it afterwards. He thinks that £300 a year would enable them to take in all their own poor.

Report on the Poor Law Inquiry

Widows with Children (Ballymote)

In Ballymoat (sic) the examination was attended among others by Dr Lougheed, dispensary surgeon, Bartholomew McKiltrick, land agent. Bridget Cummayne stated *"I am a widow and have seven children, three of them went away as they were starving. It is dangerous to sleep in the house lest it fall down. I am rearing a pig which will hardly pay half the rent, when we run out of potatoes we must live part of the year on weeds and cabbage"*. Dr Lougheed (sometimes Longheed) stated that to his knowledge the landlord wasted no time getting the widow and her children off his ground as fast as he could.

In Sligo town there were many widows, some were supported in the mendicity. There was no provision made for widows by the sessions, they depended on charity but most had to beg. With the paltry earnings of a working man it was impossible for him to make provision for his widow and family. Before the decline of the Linen trade it was possible for a woman to get a job, but following its decline poverty was dreadful.

Infirm Through Age:

In Tubbercurry most elderly were supported by their relatives. Weekly collections at two parochial churches collected no more than £3 per annum. Cheap clothing was bought and divided out amongst the most needy.

For Ballymote, the Protestant church collected £10 per annum. It was distributed to forty of the most aged or destitute parishioners without any distinction of religious opinions.

In Drumcliffe it was noted that at about 60 years of age the working classes become infirm. There were over 300 such persons in the parish 'infirm thro' age'. They were supported by their relatives, and a few by begging but not one by the richer classes except a few on Sir Robert Booth's estate. Sometimes they received remittances from their friends who had emigrated to the colonies, or to America. While their relatives could afford to give them a potato they would not beg.

The general opinion was that the existing system should continue rather than paying any tax for the support of the poor.

Dr Homan attended the examination in the parish of Kilmacshalgon. It was noted that the labouring men begin to 'break' at 50 years, and that the support of the destitute by relatives was considered a sacred duty. Poverty was the basis of any quarrel. It was felt that but for having to support their aged relations their children would be better fed and clothed. There were no alms houses and again no subscription among the gentry to support the aged, infirm and destitute poor. It was decided that some provision should be made for these unfortunate people.

In Sligo town it was noted that there were more than 500 destitute persons in the parish, infirm through age. They generally became incapable of work from fifty to sixty years.

It was observed that the heads of families considered they had a right to be supported "this support of the aged presses very severely on the children who can scarcely support them selves, and can never give the old people any better nourishment than the food they use themselves, the pota-to." There was a great reluctance to beg. "Up to the time that a young man gets married he does not feel aggrieved by the burden, but in many cases the daughter-in-law begins to object to the old man, who will first go and live in a separate room, if they have it to spare, but in the end will go to beg". The disinclination to beg was great and was only embarked on as a last resort. As there were no almshouses it was felt that there should be provision made to take care of the aged and infirm. It was also felt that extra funds to the mendicity would be sufficient.

Report on the Poor Inquiry

Able Bodied out of work: Examination at Ballymoat.

"The periods of the year at which the labourers are almost entirely unemployed, are June and July, the time between sowing and reaping; and December, January and February, from the digging of the potatoes to the beginning of the spring work. John Scanlan says, 'I live in a village in which there are 10 farmers. There are 23 families besides, who have no ground, and are depending on the wages they can get from us. We cannot give them more than four weeks work in the year; they strive to have some con-acre besides.'

To the question, whether when out of work they subsisted by begging? he answered, 'It is a general custom, every man must at some time expect it.' John Scanlan said, 'I have a brother who lived next door to me; he had seven in family besides himself and wife; he left the place, as he was loath to beg in his own country, and his family are begging'. Dr. Longheed said, 'I knew that man.' Another man said, 'I was last winter at work 'till Christmas for 6d. a day, without meat or drink. I took sick then of a pleurisy, from hard work and cold. I was seven weeks, and I did not do a turn of work. I am rejected upon that work now, though I am well, as they do not think me strong enough, and there are many stronger men to be had I had a son 22 years old, he died last September; he got sick while turning out clay in a basket on his back to manure a bog but that we are all doing'. And Dr. Lougheed adds, 'I attended that man, and am sure he died of hardship, bad food and cold

I knew he could not live the moment I saw him, as his frame was worn out with exhaustion.' Mr. Vogan says, 'Turning out clay on men's backs is a general thing here; not that the bog is too soft, but because they have neither horses nor asses to do it with.' The same man further states, 'I have about 220 perches of land and a house for 3*l*. a year. I had a lock of oats on it this year, which produced 23s.'. What did you do with the money? 'I buried my son with it. I have a rood and 17 perches of con-acre; for it I am to pay 3*l*. 2s. I will not get the potatoes out of it till I can pay the money. I have a daughter at service. I expect to get 1*l*. from her, and may be earn something myself. I will get as much of the potatoes to live on during the winter as I can pay for, and would perhaps get some one to join me in a note, and will thus perhaps get the entire. I will pay the whole by next spring work if I can; if not, I must leave some unpaid. We paid the con-acre rent last year by labour, and I was so supported while I was sick; but my boy is now dead, and I, have no help. I would be glad to work for my food rather than be idle'.

Some get credit when their own provisions are run out. James Davy says, 'If a man can get sufficient mark to join him in note, they will give him credit; if not, he may starve. If the meal is in the market 10s. a cwt., they charge 15s. I paid 8s. advance for three months' credit'.

The most destitute are the most reckless in contracting marriages. Dr. Longheed says, 'Certainly they are; to my own knowledge very young couples in this neighbourhood often marry, under a belief that nothing can render their situation worse. I frequently attempt to show them the folly of their conduct; but their general answer is, either that they trust in God, or that they can but go out; by which they mean, that they can but beg."

Report on the Poor Law Inquiry 1835

Sligo Town

A great number are out of employment from December to March; this, in the country, is not the worst time, as the greater number have a stock of potatoes; but labourers in the town are then very wretched. Mr Martin, M.P., said, 'The want of employment in the town is caused in some measure by the great influx of persons from the country'. Of the state of the labourers during the unemployed season, R. Henry said, 'During the winter quarter, half the labourers get very little work; I get then about two days in the week; but for the last three weeks I got only three days, at 1s. a day. We often have but one meal, and must be content with whatever we can get; last summer I did not taste food some weeks oftener than five times.' He further says, 'I have a wife and three children; from November to August I was sick; I caught cold while working in a store; I pledged every piece of furniture; when all was expended, my sister assisted me, and my family went to our friends and neighbours, who used to give us a basket of potatoes; I have now only a wisp of straw to lie on.' There seems to be no forethought whatsoever made use of in the contracting of marriages amongst the most destitute. James Rafferty said, 'I was married at 19, and had not 6d. even the marriage-money, that my wife's people gave us.' Those who have something are much more careful; for if a man have something, he will be looking for a fortune to match 'what he has himself'. There was a difference of opinion as to whether it was an advantage for a man to marry early or not; the greater number seemed to be in favour of early marriages, even without any provision being made for the burthen of a family. Frank Kennet said, 'I was employed when I married, but had nothing spared; what I earned in the day, I spent at night. At the time of the linen trade a wife was of great service, because then a woman could earn more than a man; but since then, marriage is poverty'. Here a number of persons said, 'They never saw a case in which a careful man and woman could not be better off married than single; in the country children can be useful to a man'. Rev. Mr Armstrong said, 'a wife is of great use to a man; she will prepare his food, make his shirt, stockings, &c.; if he have not a wife, he must have some one else to do those things.' And Dr. Kenny said, 'I think early marriages are most useful here; a man looks forward to be supported in age by his family, and thus often says, 'If God give us a family, they will support us when we are beyond work.' If a man marry at the age of 35, he will be broken down and unable to work before his children can be grown enough to support him, as a boy seldom gets more than half a man's hire till 18; but when a man marries young, his children will be able to support him before he is beyond his labour'."

Sick Poor: Examination Held in Ballymoat Town. Co Sligo.

DR. LONGHEED STATES, 'There is no fund for affording assistance to the families of those who become destitute by long-continued illness; and if such an institution could be protected from abuse, there can be no question about the immense good it would do. The diseases of the sick poor under my care strikingly show the miserable scantiness and bad quality of their food. Of an average number of 70 on the books, 25 consist of dyspepsia, indigestion, and other disorders of the stomach, arising from this cause exclusively; the same may be said of the scorbutic cases, which are seldom fewer than 10. Of consumption I have at this time seven cases, occasioned principally by insufficient clothing by day and shelter by night, besides 14 patients in inflammatory catarrh, mostly from similar causes. Of dropsies I have commonly 3 out of 70, or about 5 in the 100, when the patients are under 25 years old, and from 25 to 35 I have generally one percent more. Only last week I performed the operation of tapping on a girl of 17, whose disease was in my opinion occasioned solely by the long continued want of a diet sufficiently nutritive; and some time since I tapped a man and his wife within the same hour, under similar circumstances; indeed I scarcely know how to convey any adequate notion of the extreme destitution of the sick poor of this neighbourhood. In cases which I have attended as a midwife that required the use of forceps, it has been no uncommon thing to be obliged to borrow the door of some neighbouring cabin, overlaying it with a little straw, as the only means (in absence of any thing like a bed) of raising the patient from the floor. And the only covering which they are often able to provide for the child is of so coarse and rugged a texture as to rasp and fret the skin of a new-born infant. A very short time since I was called to attend a young married woman in labour, at a cabin to which I was told the neighbours had removed her from a hovel of too wretched a description to expect that any medical man would enter it. I found this a comparatively comfortable house covered with sods of turf, through which we could plainly see the sky over head, my own seat being a creel (a sort of basket), with a short plank laid across it; but this is the best seat I can often get in cabins where every exertion is made to accommodate 'the doctor'. I am at the present time attending the family of a poor labourer, of the name of John Denison, whose sole means of subsistence are derived from the produce of one acre of indifferent rocky ground, for which (with the hovel they live in) he pays a rent of 1s. 8s 6d. and certainly has not more than an average of 1s.6d a week wages; he has a wife and eight children, and every one of the latter are now sick in scarlet fever'."

Sick Poor: Sligo Town

There is no fund for affording assistance to the families of those who, by sickness, have become destitute. Dr. Kenny said, 'The want of any such resource almost daily becomes the cause of an amount of wretchedness, not easily conceived; the loss of a single day's labour by the husband, will very frequently cause the sale of some necessary article of clothing or furniture, and a week's illness will certainly send a very large portion of both to the pawn office, from which they are very rarely, if ever redeemed; the want of these articles of clothing must, of course, cause most severe illness to the entire family aand is the principal reason why Dropsies and Consumptions are so prevalent. 'The families of those so affected', Rev. Mr. Dunlevie and N. Stopford concurred in saying, 'are supported partly by begging and partly by the alms of their poor neighbours, who are often known, unasked, to divide with the sick their own insufficient means of subsistence.' With regard to the willingness of the poor to attend them sick of contagious diseases, Dr. Kenny says, they have a great dread of fever and small pox; in these diseases the poor are mostly, in the first instance left to the care of their nearest relation, but when such do not exist, neighbours, and even strangers, cheerfully undertake the duties of nurse. I never knew a sick person, not being, during the most alarming visitations of the Cholera, suffered to want the prompt and cheerful performance of every kind office to the very last. He further says, the difficulty is to exclude relations and neighbours from the bed-side of the sick even in the most threatening and infectious diseases.

In this district it is considered impossible for the labourer or cottier tenants to lay up any thing as a provision against sickness. The destitution caused by the short illness is very frequently the cause of destroying the few comforts of the labourer, and rendering him reckless. Dr. Kenny said, 'Nothing short of some rare and fortunate circumstance can, in most cases, enable a poor family to retrieve the consequences of even one illness of the husband, though but of moderate duration. The withholding relief from those who are ill, and unable to procure necessaries for themselves, continues them in a situation in which they must be useless to themselves and to the community, much longer than they otherwise would be, and the assistance which they receive, only in the shape of medicine, is frequently the most expensive and least efficacious'.

On this subject Dr. Kenny says, 'Of this we have daily proofs.

Dropsy is especially prevalent in this district, being perpetually induced by scanty and improper nutriment. It frequently happens that people are kept for a long time in a lingering state of recovery, who, by a moderate and temporary supply of wholesome food, might speedily be restored to health and usefulness; in such cases the most costly tonics will often be less invigorating than a single and plain meal'."

It is to be remembered that this Inquiry was conducted prior to the enactment of the *Poor Relief Act of 1838*. With this Act come the Poor Law Unions, the Poor Law Guardians, who were Justices of the peace, and members elected by the ratepayers. They had charge of workhouses, which were erected in every union area, and supervision of the dispensaries.

The Irish Commission of Inquiry reported against the grant of relief to able bodied men, but the Government nevertheless introduced Poor Relief based on the English model after a report by an English Law Commissioner who had only spent six weeks in Ireland!

[Collins-Local Government in Ireland]

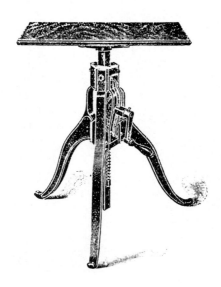

RIVERSIDE SLIGO SHOWING SLIGO GAOL

Chapter 3: History of the Gradual Development of the Health Services.

The Journals of the Irish House of Commons relate that on 15th March 1766 a committee was appointed to bring in "heads of a Bill for erecting and establishing Public County Infirmaries in the Kingdom". An Act was introduced in the reign of George III. All the buildings were originally erected by private subscription. Likewise Primary Care was initiated early in the last century as a social response to a population ailing and malnourished as a result of Famine.

The following letter, which is in my possession, written by George Beatty, Bailiff to his Landlord on 20th May 1836 Illustrates living conditions at that time.

> *"Sir, I have only received your letter from Dublin relative to Carrowpaden tenants and when I went there to distrain I found no cattle upon the lands except what would not bring in the cost of the sale of them if sold by auction and together with that I found the greatest distress prevailed amongst them for want of provisions, wherefore I concluded as the harvest is now on point of being ripe that it would be better wait for that and seize it and make it accountable for the whole than by spending time with trifles. I will let you know exactly when the time will be for you to come to Easkey for the purpose of the above mentioned."*

The Poor Law Unions came into being with the enactment of the Poor Relief Act of 1838. The Poor Law authorities consisted of Justices of the Peace and members elected by the ratepayers. They functioned in newly created areas called Poor Law Unions. These authorities were regarded as guardians of the poor. Such districts had to be of a size that would permit members of the Boards of Guardians to travel to the weekly meetings and return home on the same day. The method of travel at that time was by horse drawn transport. The administration of the Poor Law Unions lay in the hands of three Poor Law Commissioners sitting in London. In 1847 their powers were transferred to Commissioners appointed for Ireland.

According to the *Irish Poor Law Act* of 1838 any able bodied man looking for relief should be made to earn it in a workhouse where his condition would be less desirable than that of the lowest labourer outside. This was "the workhouse" test. In 1840 the *Municipal Corporations Act* was introduced for the reform of Borough Corporations.

Development of the Health Services

In 1846 the Guardians of the poor were required to provide and equip hospitals and dispensaries for the sick poor. The *Medical Charities Act* of 1851 brought changes to the Dispensary System. Government funded primary care came to Ireland in the form of 723 Dispensary Districts, each of ten mile radius, providing a patient initiated service to the poor. The Medical Officers appointed had to have a certificate of competency in midwifery and had to be over twenty three years of age. Vaccination was provided free for all. The administration of the Dispensary System was under local political control It is interesting to note that the secretary of the dispensary in most cases was the local clergyman.

The Board of Guardians who built the workhouses and Fever Hospitals in time came under the control of the the County and Borough Councils, who together with the Relieving Officers issued the blue and red tickets which entitled the patient to attend the local dispensary. The workhouses eventually became known as County Homes.

In 1863 came the Civil Registration of births and deaths, with each Poor Law Union utilized as a registration area;

Statistics of illness and mortality were compiled; prerequisites to the establishment of the Public Health Service.

The *Public Health Act* of 1879 tried to control the spread of infectious disease with clean water supplies, cleansing infected premises, proper burial ground, reduction in overcrowding in houses and destroying unsound food. The Act of 1898 was the last major change in Local Government before it came under control of the Irish Government.

In 1908 the first *Old Age Pension Act* and first *Tuberculosis Prevention Act* were passed; then The *National Insurance Act* in 1911, *School Meals Act* 1914, *Notification of Births (extension) Act* 1915. After this the First World War broke out, followed by the Civil War. The Poor Law Guardians (and Unions) ceased to operate after 1923 – functions passed to County Councils then to Health Boards. (Collins, Local Government in Ireland).

In the 1940's Tuberculosis was responsible for almost 45,000 deaths in the 20-30 year age group. The situation was aggravated by poverty, poor housing and poor nutrition. Financed by the Irish Hospital Sweepstake many more hospitals were built around this time and many sanitoria were built to deal with Tuberculosis.

In 1947 the Board of Health became an independent Government department. The School Medical Service which was introduced in 1923 was revamped in 1944. The *Health Act* of 1947 was introduced in an attempt to provide a type of National Health Service.

A White Paper on the future of the health services recommended a change from the Dispensary Service to the Choice of Doctor Scheme. With the *1970 Health Act* eight Regional Health Boards came into being to administer the new scheme to be known as the G.M.S. The *1970 Health Act* included a positive incentive to utilise hospital services, since the Health Boards were given a legal obligation to provide hospital services for the entire population. With the *1970 Health Act* the dispensaries ceased to exist and a new type of Primary Care Service was born.

BOROUGH OF SLIGO.

NOTICE.

THE PUBLIC HEALTH COMMITTEE OF SLIGO hereby call upon the Householders to put their Houses and Back Premises in a good Sanitary condition, by removing all Manure, Cabbage Leaves and Potato Peelings, perfecting the Sewerage, and Whitewashing the Yards and Premises immediately, as strict orders have been given to the Sanitary Sub-Officer to make a particular and minute inspection, and to enforce the full penalty of the Law against each defaulter. No Manure will be allowed on the Streets after 9 o'clock a m. Householders to have the space opposite their doors swept each morning before 9 o'clock a.m., and also on every Saturday night before 10 o'clock p.m.

By order.

JOHN SHEA,
Executive Sanitary Officer.

TOWN HALL, SLIGO,
May 20th, 1921.

GILLMOR, SLIGO.

42

Chapter 4: First Sligo Hospitals and Union Workhouses.

THE LYING IN HOSPITAL AND HOUSE OF REFUGE.

In 1804 the Grand Jury of Sligo voted £30 for the training of a proper nurse. Wood-Martin states that in 1819 fifty poor married lying in women were attended by the accoucheur. Various individuals bestowed monies, and fines were levied in the Borough to support those two institutions. These institutions were said to have been discontinued some time after the introduction of the Poor Law Union system with the Workhouse and Dispensary system.

It is interesting to note that in a Corporation document of 1760 mention is made of a workhouse and almshouse for the poor in Sligo.

MENDICITY INSTITUTION

In 1824 a mendicity institution was established in Sligo to relieve the suffers of the famine of 1822. It was to provide a home for the destitute poor that crowded the streets. It was established in the old 'House of Correction' close to the prison barracks in Albert Street. In the first year 50,507 meals were served to 29,753 persons. The institution, like the gaol was self supporting, and the contract for the cleaning of the streets was given to the Mendicity Institution by the old Town and Harbour Commissioners.

SLIGO UNION

The Poor Law Guardians came into being with the passing of the *Poor Relief Act* of 1838. On August 21st 1839 a first meeting was held of the Poor Law Guardians of the Sligo union. A network of areas covering the entire country was formed called Poor Law Unions. These were administered by Boards of Guardians. The *Grand Jury Act* of 1836 was adapted so that powers given to Grand Juries in relation to public works and other matters could be exercised by their successors. In 1851 the Poor Law Guardians were given the central administration of the *Nuisance Removal* and *Disease Prevention Acts,* and in the same year under their direction the Dispensary System of medical relief for the poor was organised as part of the administration of these Guardians.

The Guardians of each union were responsible for the Dispensary Service and the workhouse within their area. The Poor Law Unions persisted until 1923 when they ceased to exist and their responsibilities were transferred to the local County Councils.

The Dispensary Service persisted until 1970 when a new health service called the General Medical Service was introduced. Twelve years after the introduction of the Poor Relief Act of 1836 the then Sligo Union was divided into three areas over a period of time.

Tubbercurry Union

The Tubbercurry Union was formed on the 23rd of February 1850. The cost of erecting the workhouse according to Woodmartin was £7,400. This included the purchase of twelve acres of land. The workhouse was to provide for paupers previously in Sligo, and Swinford workhouses. The Tubbercurry union covered the dispensaries at Tubbercurry and Coolaney. Information regarding this union can be gleaned by the half yearly statement of accounts ended 25th March 1860, published by Gillmor Brothers of Ratcliffe St. Sligo. In a summary of *Indoor Pauper Relief* we learn that 77 paupers were admitted during the half year, 58 persons had been discharged in that time, 77 were still in residence and 5 persons had died. The average weekly cost per head was 2s.7³/₄d, of which 2.s. 3 ³/₄d. went on food and 4d on clothing.

In Outdoor Relief, 27 paupers were admitted to outdoor relief in that half year, and only 2 persons were on relief at the end of the half year.

Concerning salaries, the *Roman Catholic chaplain received £40 per annum; James Donohoe, Clerk and Master £90 per annum; Maria Flynn, Matron and Hospital Nurse £15; Mary McKenzie, Schoolmistress £10; Dr. James Daly Vernon £30; John Johnston, Porter £5. The cost of provisions was £178-0s5d. Clothing was £30-1s1d; printing, stationery, advertising and postage amounted to £156-5s-0d, while drugs, medicine and surgical appliances cost £6-1s-4d in the half year.*

On the 9th April 1861 Fr. John Brennan P.P. chaplain to the union, replying to a letter from his Bishop stated that the Guardians "show a kindly and liberal feeling towards the paupers". The staff were all Catholic with the exception of the Medical Officer. Fifty three of the fifty five adult inmates were Roman Catholic and 22 of the 25 children were likewise. The inmates were contented and industrious, occupied in keeping the house and grounds in order. He reported that the sanitary conditions of the inmates were good, and that sick persons though not paupers, sought on occasion admission to the workhouse hospital. He stated that the Guardians "have not given any annoyance to the chaplain, neither have they interfered with the Catholic inmates". He continued "I would not recommend outdoor relief for adults, as I think the sick and the poor will be much better attended to in a well regulated workhouse. I would, however recommend outdoor relief for foundlings and orphan children under five years of age as I believe the mortality of this class in a workhouse is greater than outside". The letter concludes "I have the honour to remain your Lordships' humble and obedient servant.".

[Correspondence from the Bishop's Library, Sligo]

THE DROMORE WEST UNION

This union was established and this workhouse opened on 1st May 1852. The paupers had been previously cared for in the Sligo and Ballina workhouses. The Dromore West union covered the Dispensary Service at Easkey, Skreen and Castleconnor.

THE SLIGO UNION

The Guardians of the Sligo Union had control of five dispensaries with seven Medical Officers, for the treatment of the sick and the indigent within the union, supplying medicine and surgical appliances for those too poor to pay. The dispensaries it controlled were at Carney, Sligo, Collooney, Ballymote and Riverstown. Again, insight into the working of this union can be gleaned from its half yearly statement of accounts ended 25th March 1860.

Indoor Paupers relieved were 284 persons who were in residence at the commencement of the half year. During that time there were 5 births; 525 persons had been admitted and 369 persons had been discharged; 41 persons had died and 403 paupers were still in residence.

The average weekly cost per head was 2s. $5^1/_2$d, of which 1s. $11^3/_4$d was spent on food and necessaries, and $5^3/_4$d on clothing. There was no outdoor pauper relief.

Salaries for the Sligo Union were as follows:

REV. M.W. JELLET, PROTESTANT CHAPLAIN	£20 PER ANNUM.
REV. JAMES CASEY, ROMAN CATHOLIC CHAPLAIN	£50 PER ANNUM.
REV JAMES HERON, PRESBYTERIAN CHAPLAIN	£10 PER ANNUM.
DANIEL CLARK, CLERK	£100 "
MICHAEL FLYNN, ASSISTANT	£35 "
JAMES FERRALL, MASTER	£60 "
CATHERINE FERRALL, MATRON	£30 "
BEDILIA O'MALLEY, SCHOOL MISTRESS	£20
DR. TRAVERS HOMAN	£80
DR. EDWARD FARRELL, ASSISTANT	£40
SAMUEL GREGG, PORTER	£10
SARAH PARSONS, NURSE	£15
ROSE CARNEY, FEVER HOSPITAL NURSE	£ 8

PROVISIONS   £744-4s-5D;   NECESSARIES   £148-6s-4d.
CLOTHING   £212-5s-4d.
REPAIRS   £56-7s-11D;
INSURANCE   £16-7s-6d;
DRUGS & SURGICAL APPLIANCES £10-15s-10d!
PRINTING, STATIONERY, ADVERTISING, POSTAGE £88-0s-9d;
FURNITURE, UTENSILS AND IMPLEMENTS OF WORK £24-156-4s.
BOOKS FOR SCHOOL £3-12s-10d.

SLIGO WORKHOUSE

This Workhouse was built in 1841 and at times accommodated over seven hundred persons. Three Auxiliary Houses had to be opened, one in Ballincar, during the famine to accommodate 4,175 persons. Later the workhouse was known as the County Home and incorporated St. John's hospital with an average of between three and four hundred inmates under the care of the Sisters of Mercy..

I am indebted to Dr. Patrick Heraughty's unfailing memory for a description of St. John's in the early part of this century. " The old complex at Ballytivnan was built as the workhouse, and later became known as the County Home. It was built around a courtyard and eventually different sections were used for different purposes. The part which housed people who were unfit to live at home was known as "the body of the house". Two wards were used as female and medical wards and known as St. John's There were two or three private medical wards. Another section was set off as the maternity wing also under the name of St. John's. The Registrar of deaths, births and marriages had his offices to the right of the Entrance Hall."

Though the name workhouse still lingers in the minds of some of the oldest residents of the town St. John's Hospital is now a fine Geriatric Hospital incorporating a day hospital and a Rehabilitation Unit.

As late as July 19th 1919 the following advertisement appeared in the *Sligo Independent*:

SLIGO UNION MALE LUNATIC ATTENDANT WANTED.

The Guardians of the above union will at their meeting to be held on Saturday 2nd August 1919 receive and consider applications from competent persons for the position of Male Lunatic Attendant in the workhouse at a salary of £20 a year, one suit of clothes, and one pair of boots with officers rations and apartment. The person appointed will be expected to carry out the duties as directed by the Medical Officer, the Master or Matron of the workhouse and conform strictly to the regulations.

By order of T. McGoldrick. Poor Law Office. Sligo 1919.

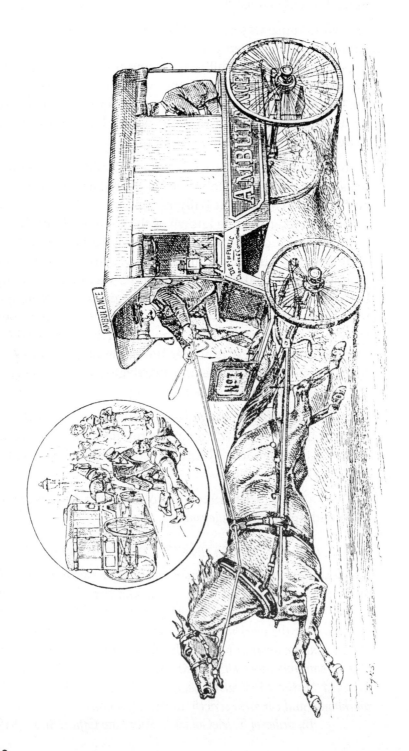

Chapter 5: The Role of Nun Nurses in the Workhouse

O n the 14th February 1898 a letter sent to the Board of Guardians of the Sligo Union from the Local Government Board in Dublin caused much concern and led to the consideration of one of the Guardians, the Roman Catholic Bishop of Elphin of allowing nun nurses to work in workhouses in the Elphin dioceses.

The letter related to a visit by the Local Government Board Inspector, Dr. Flynn to the union workhouse at Sligo. He pointed out that the nursing arrangement in the union hospital was far from satisfactory. "It appears that the present staff consists of three principal nurses, one of whom holds a certificate of training in midwifery, the other two had some hospital experience but do not hold certificates. There are also two night nurses – one for the upper hospital (female) and the other for the male hospital. In addition there are two night attendants for the idiot wards. All these it appears are untrained, and up to some time ago were paupers, but now receive a small salary and rations. The nursing staff is augmented by a large number of pauper wardsmen and one or two wards women, seventeen or eighteen in all who assist in the nursing." The Inspector observed that in the hospital proper "there are 136 patients, and in the adjoining idiot wards 33 persons, while there are also a considerable number of sick and infirm inmates occupying beds in the infirm wards who all require medical and nursing attendance".

The letter went on to state that the Guardians should consider the remodelling of the nursing staff and dispensing with pauper nursing. The report goes on to suggest the appointment of two trained nurses for night duty, and the substitution of a system of probationer nursing for that of pauper help. Extracts of the half yearly report dealt with overcrowding in two of the male wards in the infirmary, and the number of patients sleeping on the floor in the male idiot ward. The sanitary provisions especially for the women were a cause for some concern. Both the Master and Matron's stock of clothing was negligible for such an important union as Sligo.

Under Article II of the Workhouse Rules of 1897 :

1. "No pauper inmate of the workhouse shall be employed to perform the duties of nurse in the workhouse."

2. "No pauper inmate shall be employed as an attendant in the sick or Lying-in wards of the workhouse, unless such an inmate should be approved of by the Medical Officer for the purpose.

Dr. Clancy, before he allowed nursing nuns to work in the workhouses of the Elphin diocese sought the opinion of Superintendents and Medical Officers from workhouses all over the country to assist him in making his decision.

Dr. Thomas Woods, Medical Officer of Parsonstown Workhouse, in a submission stated that he had attended the poor in the workhouse hospital both before and after the appointment of the nuns as nurses. He was fulsome in his praise – the hospital was clean, cheerful and orderly since their arrival. He himself was a Protestant and had never seen any difference in their conduct to any sect or persuasion.

The Chairman of the Board of Governors of Thomastown Union in 1898 stated that in his opinion the arrival of the nuns brought great improvement to the workhouse hospital at very little cost to the ratepayer. *"I strongly recommend the employment of nuns as nurses in workhouse hospitals, as from their efficient administration they are a great financial saving. Signed, Richard Doyle J.P."*

From Carrickmacross – In 1898, the Chairman of the Board of Guardians also submitted a report in reply to an inquiry from Dr. Clancy as to the suitability of introducing nuns as nurses into workhouses. He had previously been struck by the loneliness of the sick and dying but all that had changed with the introduction of nuns as nurses.

"Strings are not produced as sheets, nor flannel bandages for blankets. Cleanliness, so necessary to the sick is scrupulously observed. The vermin pest so common in workhouses has been eradicated and no longer adds to the agony of the dying, and the condemned institution, so dreaded by the poor has already become a sought after home for the sick and dying. Signed, Norman Phelan. J.P."

The Local Government Board, November 14th 1899, in a letter to the Bishop of Limerick, a copy of which was sent to Dr. Clancy, stated that the Board invariably supported Boards of Guardians who proposed to place their hospitals under the charge of nuns. It was felt that the presence of nuns went a long way towards removing the objections to the poor sick from entering an institution such as the workhouse. The Board advocated the appointing of at least one trained nurse to the workhouse infirmary.

> "The Board were confirmed in this opinion by the recommendations made to them by the Bishops Conference at Maynooth to the effect that nuns in workhouse hospitals could not be required to attend surgical operations and this duty should be assigned to a trained nurse. Moreover it was felt that not only would it be of the utmost advantage to the nuns to have the assistance of a highly skilled nurse in the case of serious emergency, but that the appointment of such an officer would prevent certain nursing duties, which some nuns were prohibited by the rules of their order from personally undertaking, from falling into the hands of paupers or unskilled wards maids."

The report went on to explain that the nuns would not cease to be in charge of the workhouse whether or not a trained nurse was appointed. The Board had decided that nuns appointed as nurses should receive instruction and practical experience in the care and management of the sick for a definite period of time. "The standard of training thus contemplated would of course be considerably lower than is required to qualify a 'trained nurse' in the technical sense of the term." The Board considered that two years training in a union or other hospital in the case of the head nurse of the workhouse, or one years training in the case of a charge nurse would be reasonable. The Board would be glad of the Bishop's views – as to what minimum period of hospital training could be fixed in the case of nuns and whether there would be any objection to the nuns submitting to an examination and obtaining a certificate of proficiency after they had undergone the necessary tuition from competent teachers.

The difficulties that arose when nuns were changed without the knowledge of the Board of Guardians or the Local Government Board was highlighted and deplored. In the case of nuns being introduced for the first time to a work-house where there was already a head nurse, trained or untrained - this officer would have to retain her position until she died, resigned or was removed by the Local Government Board. In all cases the nuns must agree to conform to the provision of the Poor Law, and orders and regulations of the Local Government Board.

(All correspondence from the Library of the Bishop of Elphin.)

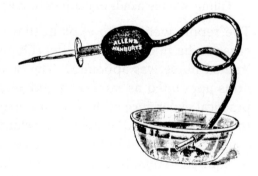

Sister Sacred Heart, Order of Mercy, Sligo Workhouse

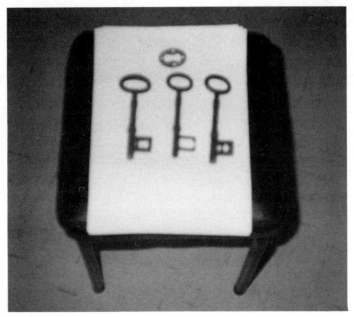

The Keys of Sligo Workhouse

DR. EFFINGHAM CARROLL MacDOWEL

Chapter 6: **Effects of the Famine**

The Poor Law Unions for the whole of County Sligo, included The Union of Sligo, Union of Dromore West, Union of Tubbercurry. It also included part of the Union of Boyle, and part of the union of Ballina.

The effect of the famine including emigration is compared over a span of twenty years. At the end of the time the Union of Tubbercurry had shown a slight recovery in its male population.

	1841	1851	1861
Co, Sligo	180,809	128,510	124,845 (61,939) (62,906 F)
Union of Sligo	77,604	58,565	53,901 (26,254M) (27,377 F)
Union of Dromore West	26,869	19,563	18,608 (9,264M) (9,344F)
Union of Tubbercurry	39,984	26,081	27,659 (13,864M) (13,793F)

In Government Papers relating to the relief of distress and the state of the unions in Ireland, the following report for Sligo Union in Co. Sligo, Jan 23rd, 1849 gives the reader some idea of the effects of the famine. The population of Sligo Union was 111,054 persons, and the valuation £148,456. This report is for 1849 before the Sligo Union was divided. According to that Report "the number of persons in receipt of relief at the present time in the union is 8,830; of which 5,834 are upon the outdoor lists.

1. This number is by no means a fair criterion of the numbers of families of able-bodied men supported, as a great number of men desert their families, go to Scotland, England and America, and leave them chargeable to the union.

2. Judging from the increase last year and present prospects, it is to be feared that during the three summer months there will be an increase of 5,000 above the present number of recipients of relief, or 14,000 in all.

3. There is £8,000 of present rate in collection, which may be counted on; but £6,500 of this is to be appropriated for the repayment of Government advances under the *Relief Act*, the remainder will of course be insufficient for the relief of the destitute; and though the guardians intend striking another rate in March next, yet before harvest it will be found impossible to collect more than a small portion of it. The obstacles to its collection are, the general inability of the farmer and gentleman classes to pay previous to harvest; the falling prices for agricultural produce; the large and several demands upon the ratepayers – two county cesses, including repayment of labour rate, being payable in the meantime (for instance, the charge now in collection of the town of Sligo is 6s-11d.), added to this the rates must necessarily be highest in the poorest districts, and vice versa, lightest in those best able to pay; so that the amount to be reckoned on previous to harvest must be small. There has been no negligence on the part of the collectors. The rates have been well collected, considering the impoverished state of the union. As to the means of the proprietors being exhausted, I say they decidedly are, although it is a difficult matter to point out proof sufficiently definite to the Commissioners; but from what I personally know of the proprietors and occupiers in this union, the bad circumstances of nearly all, the running away of the better class of tenants, and the breaking down of the inferior class, I think that the means of meeting the increasing pressure are scanty, if not entirely exhausted.

4. The causes of distress are, the successive failure of the potato in the first instance, the stagnation of employment, resulting from inability and unwillingness amongst proprietors in country districts; and in the town, from the diminution of trade, and of the large export of provisions which formerly employed a great many persons.

5. It is difficult to ascertain the quantity of potatoes at present in the union; supposed to be sufficient for seed. They are bad in quality, and not forming the same good article of consumption that they had heretofore; besides, the high prices place them much out of the poor man's reach. The kinds of food in use amongst the lower classes are Indian and oat meal, and turnips.

6. There has been no opposition to the collection of the poor rates in this union worth noticing, particularly in the collection of the last rate.

This union, I consider, has borne up well against the weight thrown on it by the effects of famine, making little noise about its misery, and not bringing its distress into notice, yet it had a large proportion of both to deal with; and taking into consideration the great and increasing poverty of the class who had to support such a disproportionate amount of pauperism, the strain upon the funds to make the income meet the expenditure, and the difficulties experienced in endeavouring to check extravagance and avoid wholesale out-door relief by procuring in-door accommodation, I think much has been done, and with much credit to the management of the affairs of the union. Its present prospects are bad: distress appears increasingly amongst a large class that will have to be supported; rates will soon be uncollectable, and much must be done to remedy the pauperism of one class, and prevent the ruin of the other."

On the 25th March 1848 the total assets of the Sligo Union were at £15,810, and its expenses £20,098, according to its balance sheet. In the month of July 1848 accommodation was provided in the workhouse for 1,968 persons, while 9,872 persons obtained out- door relief during that month.

WORKHOUSE ACCOMMODATION AVAILABLE		RELIEVED IN WORKHOUSE	AVERAGE OUT RELIEF LISTS
October	2,072	1,869	893
November	2,122	2,329	947
December	2,632	2,808	1,761

Statement for Expenses incurred year ending 29/9/1848

IN MAINTENANCE £6,789.

      SALARIES & RATES OF WORKHOUSE OFFICERS £1,242.

      OUTDOOR RELIEF £7,274.

      SALARIES OF RELIEVING OFFICERS £512.

MAINTENANCE OF FEVER HOSPITAL–

      SALARIES & EXPNS OF VICE GUARDIANS – NONE

MEDICINE PURCHASED IN THE YEAR £324

HOUSEHOLD REQUISITES PURCHASE £430

VACCINATION £49. ADDITIONAL BUILDING ALTERATION £950

CLOTHING & BEDDING £1,312

In 1848 the workhouse in Sligo was the main workhouse for the Sligo Union. It was only in 1850 that the Tubbercurry union was formed with its workhouse, and likewise in 1852 Dromore West union was established.

SLIGO COUNTY INFIRMARY

Chapter 7: Sligo County Infirmary

No records of the infirmary exist to show when it was established. It existed in the 18th century and was maintained by voluntary subscription. The census of Ireland for 1851, which is most informative states that the infirmary was established in 1765 with twenty five male and twenty five female beds. In the late 18th century Dr Burnside and Dr. Ovenden were surgeons to the infirmary. There is mention of Dr. Bilar and Dr. Coyne working there at that time. (Wood-Martin)

Dr. William Bell was surgeon in charge in 1813, but died of Cholera in 1832. The Sligo infirmary was built on the Mall 1816/1817 having moved from Chapel Lane/Street

(as per Mss. Sligo County Library).

In 1813 William Stephen Mossop, a local artist struck a medal depicting Sligo Infirmary. (Wood-Martin)

Records in the Irish Architectural Archive however, state that "the Sligo Infirmary was erected in 1824 ('*The Builder'* 1851 & 1912). "*The Sligo Infirmary was erected in 1824, pleasantly situated on an eminence on the Mall overlooking the waters and the scenery of Lough Gill, Cairns and Hazelwood. A visitor observed that the scenery and mountains were so charming, that it would be almost worth a man's while to fall ill, and become an inmate, to have an opportunity of enjoying them. In contrast to its surroundings, the infirmary was a plain institutional building of five bays, and three storeys over a basement, devoid of any ornamentation. The entrance front had a prosjecting centre bay with an eaves pediment, and tripartite windows below*". Unsigned drawings of the infirmary from the office of the Dublin contractor Henry, Mullins and McMahon are held in the Irish Architectural Archives.

"In 1850 William Deane Butler (1780-1859) was employed to carry out additions to the infirmary. These drawings show

Butler's proposal for the addition of a single bay, three storey wings, a single storey entrance porch, and extensions to the rear of the building including two four storey campanile style lavatory towers. On the principal facade Butler took the central tripartite window motif and used this in a variety of designs for the windows in the wing". In April 1851 the 'Builder' reported that the additions were in the course of construction. The attractive Victorian Italianate style of Butler's work greatly enlivened the appearance of the old infirmary, and almost doubled the accommodation available. In 1912 the infirmary underwent "necessary improvements" to the designs of Albert Murray. The infirmary was subsequently demolished circa 1965 and a 'state of the art ' modern hospital now stands in its place.

After Dr. William Bell died in 1832 of Cholera Dr. Thomas Little was appointed surgeon to the infirmary and he too succumbed to Cholera in 1849. He had been surgeon to the infirmary for 17 years. After his death he was succeeded by Dr. Edward Knott and later by the son of Thomas Little, Dr. William Swayne Little who died in 1876.

In 1854 Dr William Swayne Little wrote a letter to the 'Dublin Medical Press' in defence of county infirmaries. This letter was subsequently published. (National Library) In a Government Bill it was proposed that county infirmaries should be abolished and replaced by numerous smaller hospitals rather than having a central hospital in any one area.

Dr. Little wrote how in his opinion the existing infirmaries could be reformed. In support of the system that existed at that time he detailed that in the previous year of 732 patients treated in Sligo infirmary, 52 patients or 7% of the total were admitted from Leitrim, Fermanagh and Donegal. *"I confidently assert that Sligo Infirmary containing 80 beds is fully equal to the hospital requirements of its non destitute poor"*.

For the year 1866 the Board of Governors of Sligo County Infirmary were:

EX OFFICIO– *The Lord High Chancellor. The Lord Primate.*
The Lord Bishop of Elphin, The Vicar of Calry.

LIFE GOVERNORS: *Colonel Cooper M.P, Sir R. Gore-Booth, M.P., Earl of Orkney, William Ramsey, Jeremy Jones, Rev. G.D. Mansfield, Robert Curtis, H.H. Slade, William Phibbs, Robert G. Taylor, Robert Jones, Alexander Crichton, Richard Olpherts, Richard J. Verschoyle and the Right Rev. L. Gilhooly.*

ANNUAL GOVERNORS: *P. O'Connor (Sligo), J. Martin, Mrs Armstrong (Chaffpool), John Brett, Mrs Cooper, (Cooper's Hill), F.M. Olpherts, C.D. Fox Rev. Samuel Shone, Roger D. Robinson.*

TREASURER: *Richard Gordon,*   SURGEON *W.S. Little,*

APOTHECARY: – *Dr. Powell.*   MATRON: *Mrs Margaret Bell.*

"Governors meet the first Thursday of each month at 12 o'clock."

Subsequently the female accident ward was fitted by the Wynne Family. The twin wings that were later added almost doubled the accommodation (Wood-Martin)

According to the *Census of Ireland for 1851* from 6th January 1841 to 31st March 1851– 1680 patients were treated at Sligo infirmary. In 1877 Dr Effingham Carroll Mac Dowel, was appointed as physician and surgeon to Co. Sligo infirmary. He occupied the post for forty six years, and in the latter years was assisted by Dr. P.M.Quinn.

It is interesting to note the names on the polling list for the *Joint Committee of Sligo County Infirmary*, published by the secretary M.J.Flynn on 28th June 1914. It includes *Very Rev. Canon Doorly, Patrick Cummins, Very Rev. M. Doyle. P.P., Peter Cawley, James Hannon, Very Rev. Canon O'Connor, Jeremiah Mulrooney, John McCryan, B. J. Conlon, Rev. D. O'Grady P.P. James Flanagan, Bernard Harte, John Hennigan, James Durkin, Patrick J. Henry, Rev. Fr. Healy, Very Rev. Canon Maher, Very Rev. Canon J. P. B. Quinn, Pat McMannamy, John Connolly, Hon. Mrs Wynne, Georgina Lady Gore-Booth and Lady Crofton.*

The Annual Report of the Sligo County Infirmary for the year ended 31st March 1916 gives a great insight into the high level of care at that time. "except in cases of accidents or urgency, applicants for admission are required to attend for admission at the county infirmary on Tuesdays and Fridays at one o'clock pm. Visiting days: Tuesdays from

2.00–4.00pm; Saturdays from 2o'clock to 4.00pm; Sundays from 3.00 o'clock to 5.00 pm; Visitors may be admitted on other days on the written order of a governor".

A single donation of £21 qualifies for Life Governorship while £3.30 qualifies for Annual Governorship. Life Governor at that time was Lieu. Colonel Campbell.

ANNUAL SUBSCRIBERS: (GOVERNORS AND GOVERNESSES)
Hon, Mrs Wynne, Lady Crofton, Georgina Lady Gore-Booth, A.C O'Hara Esq. J.P. Arthur Jackson Esq. J.P. Sir Josslyn Gore-Booth, Major O'Hara.
"Concerning gifts of fruit, cake, wine etc. they must be given to the nurse in charge and not to the patient."

Dr, Effingham MacDowel in his report stated that in that year 476 interns and 1610 externs were treated, 284 of these were outside the ten mile area. Those treated in the House (infirmary) included 5 fractures of thigh, 8 of leg, 7 of fibula and ankle joint, 8 elbow joint, dislocations of shoulder 6, severe burns 7.

Among the operations performed with good results were amputation of thigh 3, of arm 1, strangulated hernia 9, cancer of breast 4, appendicitis 4, removal of tumour 13, tonsillectomy 15, adenoids 5. The House was reported to be in a good sanitary state.

NUMBER CURED:	360
NUMBER RELIEVED	109
NUMBER DIED	7
TOTAL	476 PATIENTS

The Financial statement at the close of the year included:

PROVISIONS

MEAT	£313-16-0	SUGAR:	£30-12-7
FISH & POULTRY	£16-12-1	VEGETABLES	£7-3-3
BUTTER	£66-8-1	POTATOES	£32-19-4
BACON	£21-15-0	WHISKEY & BRANDY	£1-3-5
EGGS	£52-12-3	WINE	£1-5-0
MILK	£153-16-3	SODA WATER	£0-18-3
BREAD	£84-11-5	PORTER	£0-2-11
FLOUR	£11-15-3	GROCERIES	£20-0-6
MEAL	£14-16-1	BOVRIL	£5-7-0
TEA,COFFEE & COCOA	£41-18-1	SOUP	£8-0-2

TOTAL   £891-1-11

SURGERY AND DISPENSARY

DRUGS ETC	£106-5-2	INSTRUMENTS	£31-5-1
DRESSINGS	£31-1-9		
PLUMBING	£36-0-3	CLEANING	£8-3-4
SUNDRIES	£13-5-6		

DOMESTIC

FURNITURE, BEDDING AND LINEN £44-14-8.
BLANKETS   £26-15-3.
HARDWARE, CROCKERY, BRUSHES £25-6-10.

WATER	£13-15-6	COAL	£127-10-0.
GAS	£122-4-3.		

TURPENTINE & PETROLEUM   £4-1-8.

UNIFORM	£33-1-0.	LAUNDRY	£2-5-0.
WOOD	£1-1-6.		

SECRETARY-PETTY CASH   £4-0-2.
BOOKS, PRINTING AND STATIONERY   £24-19-9.

ADVERTISING	£10-4-2.	INSURANCE:	£8-2-6. (BUILDINGS)
INSURANCE (OF OFFICIALS)	£3-8-0.		

MISCELLANEOUS £44-9-6.

SALARIES AND WAGES

MEDICAL	£129-19-0	DISPENSING	£40-0-0.
NURSING	£241-0-6	OTHER OFFICERS	£30-0-0
PORTERS	£59-14-0	DOMESTIC SERVANTS	£65-11-8.

TOTAL EXPENDITURE: £2,212 -7-9

RECEIPTS: £2,117-2-11 *including £700 supplied by County Council.*
ANNUAL SUBSCRIPTION: £22-1-0.   RENT: £20.

STATEMENT OF NAMES AND SALARIES OF OFFICERS

NAME OF OFFICER	OFFICE	SALARY/ANNUM	ALLOWANCE
M.GORDON	MATRON	£50-0-0	£3-3-0 UNIFORM
M.CONLON	NURSE	£50-0-0	£3-3-0 UNIFORM + £3 WASHING
E. McKILLOP	NURSE	£50-0-0	"
K.O'CONNOR	NURSE	£40-0-0	"
K. HARTE	SERVANT	£13-0-0	"
B. KELLY	SERVANT	£14-0-0	£3-3-0 UNIFORM
A. MONAGHAN	SERVANT	£16-0-0	"
M. NEARY	SERVANT	£12-0-0	"
CATH. FEENEY	SERVANT	£12-0-0	"
JOHN HIGGINS	PORTER (ASST)	£14.0.0.	"
PAT KEANE	PORTER	£34-0-0	£26 RATIONS +£ 4-4 UNIFORM
E. MacDOWEL	SURGEON	–	£80 HOUSE ALLOWANCE
M.J. FLYNN	SECRETARY	£30-0-0	–
DR. P.M.QUINN	SURGEON (ASST.)	–	£30 GRATUITY
P. CAGNEY	APOTHECARY	£40	

(Relative of James Cagney of Hollywood Fame)

THE COMMITTEE OFFERED THANKS TO

HON. MRS WYNNE – FLOWERS AND PAPERS.
SIR JOSSLYN GORE-BOOTH – HARES AND PHEASANTS.
LADY CROFTON – FLOWERS   MRS FOWLER – PAPERS.
MRS McCORMACK – FRUIT AND MAGAZINES.
REV. MR ORR – FLOWERS. REV. CANON ARDILL– FLOWERS & HOLLY.
MRS MacDOWEL – CLOTHES   MRS PERCEVAL – OLD LINEN.
MISS GILLMOR – PAPERS

On March 24th 1917 ('*Sligo Independent*') at the monthly meeting of the Joint Committee of Management of which Alderman E. Foley J.P. President, also present were Georgina Lady Gore-Booth, Lady Crofton, Very Rev. Canon Daly, and Mr Cawley Co.C., Mr A Kilfeather (Sec.).

Dr. Mac Dowel referred to the treatment of soldiers in the infirmary. He said that they had already treated men from the county but the authorities had decided on the establishment of a central hospital in or near Dublin, and that Sligo would be asked to contribute.

On August 1920, at a special meeting of the Committee of Management of the County Sligo Infirmary, Father Currid presiding, Dr. Mac Dowel submitted the following report

"I have been asked to make remarks as to the external department of the County Hospital. For over forty years the system has been to have two extern days Tuesdays and Fridays – every week. On these days people attend from all parts of the county, and they must bring a Governor's ticket. Only those are admitted that are suitable for treatment. Many chronic or incurable cases are advised to get treatment elsewhere. A considerable number of minor accidents, and surgical cases attend during the week and these are treated. These include wounds, ulcers, sprains, and various like injuries. For such things the infirmary is of great convenience to the general public, as we have always on hand properly sterilised dressings, bandages etc. All accidents are admitted at all hours. It is generally suggested that they should have a doctor's letter, particularly if first treated outside. But the general public are really not treated on our extern days. This is the work of the dispensaries. We don't give medicine except in exceptional and surgical cases. I think this system has worked well. I would suggest, however, that it would be well if separate mornings were used for the ex soldiers as it would prevent overcrowding. It should be understood that chronic and incurable cases are more suited for treatment in the district hospitals, and that the county hospital should be used for the treatment of acute cases, medical and surgical, including of course all accidents, which I have previously stated should be treated at all hours, as delay in the treatment of wounds is often the cause of subsequent trouble. The county Sligo Infirmary would be better designated 'Sligo County Hospital', as the word 'infirmary' sounds as if this hospital was to be used for the infirm and old people, while the reverse is true."

(Sligo Champion 21/8/1920.)

The Sligo County Hospital was said to open in 1940, but did not actually open until 1942. Prior to this all maternity and medical cases were treated in a section of the County Home under the care of Dr. Hugh McLaughlin. All cases that warranted caesarean section were operated on by surgeon Charles McCarthy in the infirmary. After the Sligo County Hospital was opened the medical and maternity cases were transferred there, still under the care of Dr. Hugh McLaughlin. Dr. McCarthy carried out gynaecological operations there, as required. Nurse Maguire, who was in charge of the maternity section in the County Home moved to the Sligo County Hospital in the same capacity. Dr. McLaughlin died around the year 1947. (Dr. Heraughty – personal letter).

Gradually the services extended – Dr. William Donovan was appointed Obstetrician and Gynaecologist. Dr. John Fox was appointed the first Radiologist. Mr. Thurloc Swan succeeded Dr McCarthy as Co. Surgeon, some time after the former's retirement. Mr Swan is a nephew of Dr. Harold Swan who was in practice in Wine St. in the early part of this century, and is a cousin of Dr. Jeremy Swan (see later).

Dr William Wren and later Dr. Jeremiah Twomey were appointed as anaesthetists.

On the medical side Dr. Desmond Ryan was appointed County Physician, Dr Bryan McMahon later held the post for a number of years until Dr Dermot M.Collins was appointed permanently and held this post until his retirement. Dr. Niall O'Donohoe from Crumlin Hospital held a Paediatric Clinic each month for a number of years. Likewise Mr Maurice O'Connor (Jervis St. Hospital) and later Mr Tom Keane (Richmond Hospital) held E.N.T. Clinics.

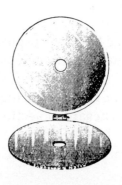

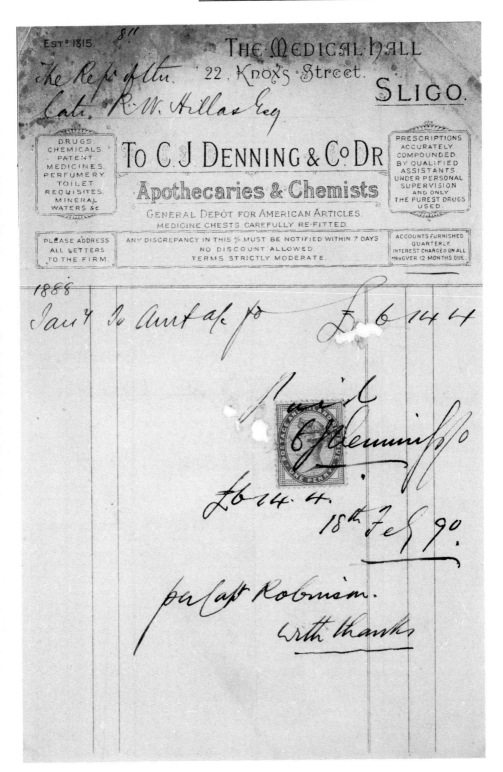

Est⁰ 1815   8"

THE MEDICAL HALL

The Reps of the   22, Knox's Street.

Cat. R.W. Hillas Esq   SLIGO.

| DRUGS, CHEMICALS, PATENT MEDICINES, PERFUMERY, TOILET REQUISITES, MINERAL WATERS &c. | To C.J. DENNING & Co DR | PRESCRIPTIONS ACCURATELY COMPOUNDED BY QUALIFIED ASSISTANTS, UNDER PERSONAL SUPERVISION AND ONLY THE PUREST DRUGS USED. |

Apothecaries & Chemists

GENERAL DEPÔT FOR AMERICAN ARTICLES.
MEDICINE CHESTS CAREFULLY RE-FITTED.

| PLEASE ADDRESS ALL LETTERS TO THE FIRM. | ANY DISCREPANCY IN THIS % MUST BE NOTIFIED WITHIN 7 DAYS NO DISCOUNT ALLOWED. TERMS STRICTLY MODERATE. | ACCOUNTS FURNISHED QUARTERLY. INTEREST CHARGED ON ALL OVER 12 MONTHS DUE. |

1888

Jan 4 To Amt a/c p o   £ 6 14 4

Paid

£6 14 4

18th Feb 90.

per Capt Robinson.

With thanks

SLIGO: *Medical Care In the Past*

SLIGO ASYLUM

Chapter 8: The District Lunatic Asylum

Prior to the erection of the present building a few harmless lunatics were kept in a house, the ruins of which are said to be about two miles from Sligo on the Rosses Point Road. (Wood-Martin). As late as 1828 the jail afforded an asylum to lunatics. In 1831 thirty were thus confined, but by March 1849 this was reduced to only fourteen. The asylum itself, a most imposing building was built in 1852. The architect was Mr Deane Butler, and Mr Caldwell of Sligo was the builder. Mr John Battle of Collooney was clerk of works.

The main structure cost £35,199 but in 1874 due to an increase in the number of registered lunatics two additional wings were built on at a cost of £18,000 which increased the accommodation from 250 to 470 beds!

According to O'Rourkes 'History of Sligo' in the year 1886 there were 217 patients from Sligo and 187 from Leitrim. The expenditure was £7,756-16-2 for that year.

Dr. John McMunn was appointed the first Resident Medical Superintendent in 1852, and he died in 1882. He was succeeded by Dr. Joseph Petit, and his assistant was Dr. G.R. Lawless. Dr. Petit was forward thinking and favoured as far as possible the abolition of restraints which up to that time were regarded as indispensable in the asylums of the country. Instead of caging in-patients he allowed them recreation to move around the extensive grounds and exercise as they thought fit. He removed doors from dormitories to impress the sense of freedom in the minds of all. He is said to have been an authoritarian figure who would stride up and down the corridors outside while the Board of governors was meeting in chambers!

Thom's Directory of 1855 lists :

JOHN MCMUNN RESIDENT PHYSICIAN, AND WILLIAM SWAYNE LITTLE CONSULTING PHYSICIAN TO SLIGO MENTAL ASYLUM.

1878 JOHN MCMUNN R.M.S.,   JAMES MCMUNN ASSISTANT R.M.S.

1880 DR JOHN MCMUNN R.M.S. DR. R.P. HETHERINGTON ASST. R.M.S.

1881 DR. HON MCMUNN R.M.S., DR. G.R. LAWLESS ASSISTANT R.M.S.

1884 DR. JOSEPH PETIT R.M.S. ,   DR. G.R. LAWLESS ASSISTANT R.M.S.

1898 DR JOSEPH PETIT R.M.S. DR. THOMAS GILCRIEST ASSISTANT R.M.S.

(sometimes written as Gilchrist)

1921 DR. JOSEPH PETIT R.M.S. , –LAST APPEARS IN THOM'S DIRECTORY

1922 DR. THOMAS GILCHRIST ACTING R.M.S.

1923 DR. PATRICK O'DOHERTY R.M.S. IN 1926.

There were 740 patients committed to his care.

1928 DR. PATRICK O'DOHERTY R.M.S. – DR. THOMAS GILCHRIST ASSISTANT M.O.

1930 DR PATRICK O'DOHERTY R.M.S. *last appears in Thom's Directory.*

1931 DR. JOHN DUNNE R.M.S.,   DR. THOMAS GILCHRIST M.O.

1933 DR. THOMAS GILCHRIST LAST APPEARS IN THOM'S DIRECTORY.

1935 DR JOHN DUNNE R.M.S.,   DR. J.J. WALSH ASSISTANT M.O.

1937 DR JOHN DUNNE R.M.S.,   DR. T FOLEY, ASSISTANT M.O.

1939 DR. JOSEPH KEARNEY R.M.S.. DR. T. FOLEY ASSISTANT M.O., DR. M.H. MCDONAGH TEMPORARY ASSISTANT M.O.

1941 DR. T. FOLEY, ACTING R.M.S. DR. T.H. QUINN AND DR. M.H. MCDONAGH TEMP. ASST. M.O.

1943 DR. C.J.MCCARTHY R.M.S., *(not to be confused with Dr. Charles McCarthy, Co Surgeon)*   DR. T. FOLEY ASST M.O.

1944 DR.C.J.MCCARTHY R.M.S., DR.T. FOLEY AND DR. JAMES CLYNE ASSISTANT M.O'S

1945 DR. T. FOLEY R.M.S.;   DR. JAMES CLYNE ASSISTANT M.O.; DR. SHEILA HENRY

1946 DR. T. FOLEY R.M.S.   DR. JAMES CLYNE ASST. M.O. DR. KEVIN WALSHE ASST. M.O.

1960 DR. T. FOLEY RMS.   DR. JAMES CLYNE ASST. M.O DR. SHEILA DEVINS, DR BERNADETTE SWEENEY, DR. EMILY TWOMEY, ASST. MEDICAL OFFICERS.

Dr. John Dunne was a larger than life person about whom many anecdotes are related. He left Sligo to become R.M.S of St. Brendan's, Grangegorman mental hospital, Dublin.

Later he became the first Professor of Psychiatry in Ireland, and in 1955 the President of the Royal Medico-Psychological Association.

In the year 1866 the Board of the Sligo and Leitrim Hospital for the Insane consisted of :

Resident Physician: John McMunn M.D.; Consulting Physician: William Swayne Little; Apothecary: John Lougheed; Matron: Mrs Margaret Benson; Clerk: Robert Browne; Protestant Chaplain: Rev. E. Day; Roman Catholic Chaplain: Rev. J. Morris.

Governors: appointed by the Lord Lieutenant in Council included: Charles W. O'Hara (Chairman), Annaghmore, Collooney; Sir Robert Gore-Booth M.P., Lisadell; Lieutenant Colonel Barrett, Rathanna, Sligo; Richard Brinkley, Fortland, Easkey; Rt. Hon the Earl of Leitrim, Lough Rynn, Mohill; Colonel Cooper M.P., Markree Castle; Right Rev. Dr. Gillooly, Sligo and others.

It was noted that in all cases patients should be sent direct to the Hospital and not through the gaols. "A shilling adhesive stamp should be affixed to the declaration in the admission form."

(Sligo-Independent ALMANAC).

In the *Annual Report of the Sligo District and Lunatic Asylum of 1906* Page 15 (Irish Architectural Archives)

TOTAL LUNATICS ADMITTED FOR THE YEAR ENDING DECEMBER 1905:

    MALE: 75;   FEMALE: 59;   TOTAL : 134;

TOTAL IN ASYLUM OF DEC 31ST 1905:

    MALE: 401;   FEMALE: 270   TOTAL: 671;

Causes of Insanity P.15 Table V

MORAL CAUSES:	MALE	FEMALE	TOTAL
DOMESTIC TROUBLE	2	5	7
ADVERSE CIRCUMSTANCES	–	–	–
MENTAL ANXIETY AND WORRY	6	4	10
RELIGIOUS EXCITEMENT	0	2	2
LOVE AFFAIRS INCLUDING SEDUCTION	0	0	0
FRIGHT AND NERVOUS SHOCK	8	12	20

PHYSICAL CAUSES:

INTEMPERANCE IN DRINK	12	0	12
INTEMPERANCE –SEXUAL	0	0	0
VENEREAL DISEASE	0	0	0
SELF ABUSE (SEXUAL)	0	0	0
ACCIDENT OR INJURY	2	0	0
PREGNANCY	0	0	0
PARTURITION AND PUERPERAL STATE	0	1	1
UTERINE & OVARIAN DISORDERS	0	0	0
PUBERTY	0	0	0
CHANGE OF LIFE	0	0	0
FEVERS	0	0	0
DEPRIVATION & STARVATION	0	0	0
OLD AGE	0	0	0
OTHER BODY DISEASE & DISORDER	1	2	3
HEREDITARY INFLUENCE	31	20	51
CONGENITAL DEFECTS	0	2	2
TOTAL PHYSICAL CAUSES	48	27	75

Personal perusal of a large 'Male Casebook Register' which commenced in 1908 reveals a number of interesting facts. In a survey of the notes of 243 male patients extending over a period of forty years – eleven of the patients were under twenty years when first admitted. The cause of death *under twenty years of age* in three cases was given as pulmonary Tuberculosis and one case of Hydrocephalus. At least three of these eleven patients were mentally handicapped.

Between the age of *twenty and thirty years* there had been sixty one admissions, fifty eight of whom were single. The cause of death in the age group was listed in seven cases as due to Tuberculosis, one man died from influenza, another man from enteric fever. One resident died from cardiac failure after seven days of tonsilitis. The cause of death of another young man was registered as maniacal exhaustion.

In the age group of men between *thirty and forty years*, sixty patients were admitted, forty eight were single and twelve were married. The cause of death in this age group was registered as follows: – Pulmonary Tuberculosis (17); exhaustion of Epilepsy (2); acute Cellulitis of neck (1); Exhaustion of Melancholia (2); Dementia and Diarrhoea (1); Exhaustion of Mania (1); Cerebral Degeneration (1) Pneumonia (1); Pleurisy (1); Bronchitis and Debility (1)

In the *age group 40-50years* 25 men were admitted, 13 were single and 12 were married. The cause of registered death in the group was Pulmonary Tuberculosis (5); Exhaustion of Melancholia (4); Maniacal exhaustion (2); Pneumonia (2); general paralysis(1); Bronchitis and Syncope (1); Cerebral tumour (1) Enteric fever (1) Myocarditis (1); Cerebral degeneration (1).

The case notes of these patients showed that over the years, they either stayed as inmates or were discharged and read-mitted.

There were forty deaths recorded for those *over fifty years of age* only four of whom died of Tuberculosis. This included senile decay (8); Exhaustion of Melancholia (4); Maniacal exhaustion (1); Cholera Encephalitis (1); Senile Chorea (1) status Epilepticus (2) Debility and Dementia(3).

During these years there was a famous matron, Maggie Lawlor, who was married to Dr. Gilchrist. She ran the Asylum for over forty years and was a great friend of Senator Arthur (Fatty) Jackson who was Chairman of the Board of Governors at that time. Dr. Tim Foley, who was R.M.S. in the latter years recalls these events in a personal letter, and mentions particularly the hospital band.

Dr. Gilchrist retired to Dromahair. During the war he would travel by pony and trap and would come, via Sweetbriar Avenue – the road connecting the Calry and Hazelwood roads, to visit a patient in Doonally. After the War Hazelwood House was for some time used as an annex of Sligo Mental hospital.

COUNTY SLIGO HOSPITAL 1840-42

Chapter 9: Sligo Fever Hospital and an Account of the 1832 Cholera Epidemic.

This hospital was erected in 1822 at the joint expense of the county and Edward Synge Cooper M.P. It was built in a year of famine. The *Irish Distress Committee* in London collected £304,108.00 for famine relief. Mr Cooper spent £150/week employing persons building the Fever Hospital.

The Census of Ireland 1851 tells us that the hospital was established in 1822, that it consisted of twenty five male and twenty five female beds.

Dr Henry Irwin M.D., first physician to Sligo Fever Hospital and Dispensary recorded a severe outbreak of Cholera Asiatica as it occurred in Sligo during the months of August and September 1832. It is a fascinating account and is reproduced in full.

"Having being placed in circumstances particularly suited for observing, minutely, the late formidable epidemic which attacked this Town; and conceiving it to be the duty of all so circumstanced, to communicate what may have come to their knowledge, I am induced to furnish a sketch of the Cholera Asiatica, as it occurred in Sligo–

On Sunday, the 29th of July, the first decided case of Cholera was seen by Doctor Coyne, near to Mr. Walkers, of Rathcarrick, about three miles from this Town; and, it appeared,that at Manionstown, a bathing village,and a short distance from Mr. Walker's, and in the cabins in the neighbourhood, as well as in some extending towards Cullinamore, there were several affected with symptoms of the disease , and that two, if not three, had died of it –

Many had, a short time previous, come there, from the neighbourhood of Longford, where Cholera existed, for the purpose of sea-bathing. The inhabitants, partly from ignorance, and partly from anxiety to exonerate themselves from the charge of being infected, a feeling but natural, as they principally subsist at this season by letting lodgings to sea-bathers, violently and pertinaciously asserted, that the disease was not among them, and threatened vengeance against the medical man who reported the facts. At an early hour, on the 31st of July, an unfortunate woman of the Town was seized with the disorder, on the Barrackhill, after exposure in the streets during the night, in a state of intoxication, and died at 2 o' clock, P.M., Of that day; she was reported to have been lately at Westport, where the disease prevailed. From this day, 'til the 10th of August, no case presented itself; though it is said, and I believe, with truth, that several occurred, but were concealed, from the reluctance generally felt to acknowledge the existence of the complaint. On this day one case was admitted into hospital, and on the following days others 'til it became an overwhelming calamity.

It is right to consider what chiefly contributed to give it this character, in addition to the Almighty fiat. For myself, I am persuaded the inhabitants had much cause to blame themselves. The Board of Health took the precaution early to have the houses of the poor whitewashed and cleaned, both inside and outside, under the superintendence of the Officers of Health. As the disease approached, too, having the awful warning of Galway and Tullamore before them, it was urged by the medical men, who were members of the Board of Health, that sufficient Hospitals and Attendants should be provided; feeling that such accommodation, properly prepared, would alleviate much of the misery that must at first occur, and thus prevent the contagion spreading, as well as meet other causes of distress, by removing, at the onset, those who might be affected with the complaint – bearing in view the propensity of the poorer classes, to press around their sick neighbours, as well as the waking, and all the other fearful scenes that must take place if left in their houses, besides the dying and the dead. The Board, fully impressed with the necessity of attention to these points, nominated medical attendants, fitted up St. John's school house with thirty bed-steads, in the vicinity of the most thickly-inhabited part of the Town, and was in the act of proceeding with the preparation, when a violent outcry arose among those living in the crowded streets in the neighbourhhod. They forwarded to the Provost a memorial, signed by most, if not all, protesting against the measure; and it was also rumoured, that the first patient sent to it, should be the signal of its demolition. This Hospital was given up. It was then proposed to convert the Fever Hospital into a Cholera one, and to provide accommodation for the Fever cases elsewhere. This was also met, by angry protestations, by those living near to any suitable place suggested. Thus it was, when a ruffianly mob, armed with clubs, came in from the neighbouring country, backed by the poorer classes of the town, declaring that they would have no Board of Health, no Cholera Hospitals, and as they expressed it, they would conquer here as they had done in other places. They had, in fact, previously exhibited similar scenes at Carney, Riverstown, Ballymote, and other small towns in the county, where it had been proposed to establish Boards of Health, and had interrupted the respectable inhabitants who were disposed to take all necessary precautions to meet the impending danger. They grossly insulted likewise the medical gentleman sent to inspect and report upon the cases at Manionstown. The Board thus obstructed, I may say paralysed, was unprepared for the destruction which now occurred. All the servants who were engaged, and had promised to be ready when called upon, alarmed by the threats, and the hazardous duties to be performed, withdrew or held back from such a dangerous employment. The patients were poured into the Fever hospital in the worst stage of Cholera, while some of the Fever patients were still in it; there being no other place, as stated before, where they would be permitted to be put. The only servants who could then be procured, were many of them the most abandoned of both sexes, and to these it was necessary to give extravagant wages, several of whom, from their drunkenness and inattention, we were obliged almost immediately to dismiss. The harassing duties that devolved on the medical men, under these circumstances, may be imagined, but cannot be described.

I feel it a duty here to notice a communication made about this time, by the the secretary of the central Board of Health, 'That the resident Superintendent Medical men were too highly paid.' I need scarcely say how painfully was the reflection felt by those against whom it was levelled, though I rejoice to add, that it in no degree abated their zeal in the discharge of the important duties they were engaged in; yet it was determined by all who might survive, to repel the charge of mercenary feeling on their part, which they conceived was conveyed by the observation. They, of course, rejected not a fair return for their exertions, and the sacrifices they made of private practice. The late Doctor Coyne, and the writer of this article, were originally selected by the Sligo Board of Health for this duty, and as it became more onerous, the late Doctor Leahy and the late Mr. Bell, Surgeon to the County Infirmary, were successively added; it may be asked, what remuneration could repay the families of those who fell in the discharge of these duties? It should be recollected too, that the expense incurred was to be ultimately defrayed by the County, that it was awarded by the Board of Health here, of which the President, the Secretary and other Members, were all in the confidence of the most respectable inhabitants of the County, and were not likely to recommend what could reasonably be considered, as extravagant remuneration, for such services, witnessing as they did, the sacrifices made, the risks run and the duties performed by the medical men in question. That the risk was not imaginary suffice it to say, that Doctor Coyne, Doctor Leahy, and Mr Ball, fell victims of the disease, being three out of four appointed to this duty; leaving families and an extensive circle of friends deeply to deplore their loss. — Among the other Resident Medical men attached to the duties of the Hospital, Doctors' Knott and Powell, with Messrs. Murray, Carter Christian and Tucker suffered more or less from attacks of the epidemic. Of the medical practioners in the town, unconnected with the hospital duties, Messrs. Anderson, Beatty, Church and Sherlock died, while Doctors Carter, Devitt, and Messrs. Armstrong laboured under it in slighter degrees.

It appears to me that the number of Medical men attacked by the disease, who were especially exposed to it, goes far to set at rest the long disputed question, of its contagious or infectious quality. In truth this was impressed upon me at every step, as individuals of the same family were in a great many instances successively attacked; particularly those in close attendance upon the sick. I cannot agree with Dr. Brown (although throughout his account generally of this disease, in his excellent statement of it, as it occurred at Sunderland, he advocates the contagiousness of it) where he says 'where the disease has appeared in a private family, in a situation of life above the labouring class, it has been confined, so far as the writer's knowledge extends, and he is of opinion that he is acquainted with the circumstances of all the cases of the kind which have occurred, to the individual first attacked, and has not in any instance spread to the other members of the family, nor have in these instances, nurses or other casual attendants on the sick suffered though belonging to a class more obnoxious to the disease'. This I must say is it variance with the course of events here – among others I may state that Mr. Knott of Battlefield, at the time residing in Sligo, took the disease and died; shortly afterwards Miss Phibbs, who went from her house to attend upon Mr. Knott, fell a victim to the disease; subsequently Mr. Knott's son took the disease and also sunk under it, while Mrs Carter, the sister of Miss Phibbs, who went to attend upon her, was attacked and narrowly escaped, besides a Man and Maidservant at Mr. Knott's took it likewise but recovered. Mr. Holmes, the Collector of Excise, was attacked, and afterwards his mother-in-law, grand child and son-in-law, all of whom died. Such instances could be multiplied, but I think it unnecessary to dwell upon them. Besides it may be observed that many in the immediate neighbourhood exposed to the same

Sligo Fever
Hospital
now
demolished.

serial miasm, but who kept themselves otherwise secluded were totally exempt. – The advantages of seclusion, it is proper to state, were marked, in the Charter School, where a single case did not occur; the Barrack, and the jail, where strict seclusion was also attended to, suffered comparatively little or nothing.– The servants of the hospital furnish another proof of its contagiousness, as they were attacked beyond all due proportion: several of the porters sickened, and scarcely a nurse escaped, while many of both classes died. It is true, that a few who kept themselves secluded with the utmost care fell victims to the disease while others who were exposed in every way, escaped, as if they were unsusceptible of it. But these I would be inclined to consider as exceptions to the general rule. Upon the best consideration I am able to to give it, after weighing well all that I have witnessed or read, upon the subject, my belief is, that it is under certain circumstances Epidemic, and when concentrated, as it was here, that it becomes contagious or infectious for these terms are so often used synonymously that I think it better to use them as productive of similar effects.

I cannot avoid the impression that the season, (the dog day,) being the period when indigenous Cholera most frequently prevails contributed much to the severity of the disorder, as we had it here. The weather at its commencement was settled and serene, but after a few days, became damp and close, at which time Cholera raged with its greatest violence. This continued with little intermission till the end of August, when we had occasional brisk breezes from the north. The Barometer

No. 108   SLIGO UNION.   *N. P.*

Net Annual Value, £ *213*: — :

No. in Rate Book...................   House, &c., *Lavally*

DRUMCOLLUMB ELECTORAL DIVISION.

RECEIVED the *20* day of *February* 1897 from Mr. *Charles Robinson Per Mrs Anne Wood Martin* *Nineteen* Pound *ten* Shilling and *Six* Pence of the Poor's Rate for Drumcollumb Electoral Division, made the *27* day of October, 1896, as stated on the back of this Receipt.

£ *19 : 10 : 6* Rate
£ : : Arrears   .... *Alexander Hunter* Collector.

Kilgannon, Printer, Sligo.

DUPLICATE FOR LANDLORD.

No. 108   SLIGO UNION.   *N. P.*

Net Annual Value, £ *213*. — :

No. in Rate Book...................   House, &c., *Lavally*

DRUMCOLLUMB ELECTORAL DIVISION.

RECEIVED the *20* day of *February*, 1897 from Mr. *Charles Robinson Per Mrs Anne Wood Martin* *Nineteen* Pound *ten* Shilling and *Six* Pence, of the Poor's Rate for Drumcollumb Electoral Division, made the *27* day of October, 1896, as stated on the back of this Receipt.

£ *19 : 10 : 6* Rate
£ : : Arrears   .... *Alexander Hunter* Collector.

Kilgannon, Printer, Sligo.

ranging generally during this time between 29-30 and 30-30, and the Thermometer from 50 to 75 of Fahrenheit. The malady continuing at its height for nearly three weeks, then gradually declined. The situation of Sligo would favour its dissemination, it is surrounded by hills, and lies as it were at the bottom of a basin, although' the river winding through it tends in general, with the breaks between the hills, to its thorough ventilation, excepting when the weather is remarkably calm and damp as was the state of it at the period alluded to.

To enter minutely into the medical history and treatment of the complaint, is foreign to my purpose, and I conceive would be superfluous, after the numerous, lucid, and able publications on these subjects,. Indeed, I feel it would be worse than nugatory to dwell upon them. Suffice it to say, that we had it, I believe, in every form; that on the first days the more violent cases early sank, and few of those who became collapsed and blue, at this time, ever rallied. Stimulants internal and external, heat and frictions, with large and repeated doses of Calomel and Opium, were freely as well as perseveringly administered. Many recovered under these and other remedies, and some even with little or no medical aid; numbers, however, fell victims to the disease under every plan of treatment hitherto recommended. Of this, however, I am convinced, that although the many remedies in use, will often prove of the greatest benefit, there is still required as a desideratum, a means of treatment, that will be generally successful, in the collapsed and blue stage, or preventative of it; notwithstanding the numerous, and highly lauded nostrums, for this purpose. With respect to the saline treatment, it was tried only in a few cases, and those of the milder form, and where it appeared to me that any rational means of cure would have been likely to succeed; I must confess that I saw few disposed to depend upon it, in the severer cases, such as occurred in the earlier attacks of the disease here, nor would I at the time be inclined to sanction, so apparently ineffectual a remedy, in a disorder requiring such prompt and decided measures. It is true, in the latter days of its prevalence here, the Cholera assumed (as in almost all other places) a milder character, and became more manageable, and it was principally at this time that the saline treatment was had recourse to. As to saline injections, the questionable evidence of their utility, now before the public, deterrred us from trying them—. The consecutive Fever has been here, as elsewhere a most formidable part of this complaint, and notwithstanding all that has been written and published, much remains to exercise the industry and ability of future observers, on the pathology, as well as the therapeutical management of this stage of the disease.— Bleeding with leeches, and blistering, where the cerebral or abdominal viscera were principally engaged, with the saline effervescing minture, deluenta and diaphoretics, such as Dover's powder were the remedies chiefly used in the early part, and as it advanced, when symptoms of debility supervened, wine and other tonics were given. Reasoning a priori would lead one to suspect that the stimulants and other remedies necessary to prevent, or remove the state of collapse, would tend to cause or aggravate the cerebral and gastro enteric symptoms so frequent in this stage. Yet I must say, that in several instances where I have seen them freely used, the collapsed stage was followed by little or no subsequent Fever, and in others where they were not had recourse to, I have seen the conscecutive Fever in the severest form, and of this I am persuaded that where mercury affects the mouth, this stage does not occur, or if it should, in a very mitigated shape.

My principal object, however, is to give a concise, and connected account of the disease as it occurred here, and to warn others against the misfortunes we were led into, through the violence and brutal outcry of the populace, and with the view, that they may, as far as human means will admit, endeavour to avert so formidable a visitation. I cannot too strongly deprecate, the base and general opposition, that has almost in every place, been raised against all preparations to meet it. What is expense, which is the chief objection, in comparison with the security to life, that timely and appropriate measures would insure? Let any one contemplate the scenes that occurred here: they more nearly resemble the fictions of the older poets, where they represented the occurrences in the infernal regions, than anything else I can imagine. Men and women, screaming, and shrieking, as they followed the bier, the bearers, or the rumbling cart, containing their dead, or dying wives, husbands and children; horror displayed in every countenance, and shocking incidents on every side, such as children being left, of all ages from the most helpless infancy, parentless. The strongest minds were scarcely proof against such scenes of horror, the more nervous soon became affected with bowel complaints, which made them more prone to, and easier victims of the disease. Again, I contend that much of this may be obviated, if the complaint be early, generally, and fairly contemplated; it is therefore that I urge a fitting state of preparation, as indispensably necessary; hospitals well appointed, with a firm and well ordered police, who under the proper authorities, would insist on the early removal to the hospital, of those attacked; but above all, that the populace be warned by their Pastors and others; possessing influence over them, of the bad effects of panic, and especially of the necessity there would be, for the energetic co-operation of all in carrying into effect, the regulations suggested for the general good. Thus, I am convinced, much of the misery may be prevented, that without such precautions, must inevitably occur.

The population of Sligo, as taken at the last census, amounted to between fifteen and sixteen thousand, of these, two thirds at least left town, within a few days after the commencement of the complaint, and it will appear by a reference to the annexed numerical return, that the total attacked up to this date, of those who remained, would be nearly one in four, being 1230, and of these 641 died, which is a proportion of more than one in two: this, however, is not correct, as many had the disease, in various degrees, in whom it was concealed for there was a reluctance in almost every family to admit that it was infected, and it was only when the disease became too serious to escape notice, that the district Inspectors were enabled to detect it. The numerical return of the hospital for the same period, which is also annexed, gives a still more appalling view of the fatality that occurred therein, the number admitted being 470, while the deaths amount to 317; by this it will appear that nearly two out of three died. It should, however, be considered, that none but the worst cases were sent to Hospital from the reluctance of the poor to going there, that many were brought in actually dying, and numbers who did not survive an hour after admission, and of whose recovery there was not the slightest chance. The subject of admitting them in this state was warmly discussed by the medical men attached to the Hospital, and particularly objected to, by the younger men, but it was considered that the removal of them, even at this late period, would be of material benefit, as it would obviate a source of contagion, as well as withdraw from their friends and families, a horrid spectacle, which it is to be feared, often proved a fruitful means of predisposition to the malady. With these views, and trusting that when the motives when explained, they would do away the obloquv that must otherwise attach to the Hospital, the males were only 188, while the females amounted to 282, being nearly a hundred more out of a total of 470. This, when added to the circumstances, of there being a large proportion of them aged, and unhealthy, is corroborative of the generally received opinion, that the disease is more frequent and fatal, among the poor and infirm. Another circumstance which I am desirous of bespeaking attention to is the rapidity with which the disease ran up, as to the numbers admitted as well as deaths, to the 24th of August: then as rapidly diminishing, and becoming milder too in it character.

I may in conclusion, *be permitted to hope,* that those who escaped the destruction that occurred, are thoroughly sensible of the mercy vouchsafed to them, and that the great disposer of all events, who alone is capable of bringing good out of evil, will render it a blessing, by leading them to a more serious consideration of their religious duties, and that like the raging hurricane, when its ravages are abated, it may have left what remains in a more healthful and purified state."

It is interesting to read this report from the first Medical Officer of the Fever Hospital recorded by Dr Henry Irwin concerning the epidemic, in which so many Sligo doctors and nurses gave their lives in the care of their patients.

A brief description of the Sligo Cholera epidemic by Ritchie in 1838 is included here "a line was drawn around the town, beyond, which there was no escape, and those who attempted were driven back as into a grave. Nothing was heard in the streets but the sound of lamentation and despair. Mr Fausset, the Provost rode in every morning from the security of his county home to visit the hospitals, bury the dead, preserve order in the streets, and take his seat as the President of the Board of Health. In spite of his unrelenting labours one morning he saw the grounds of the Fever Hospital covered with unburied corpses and then as he expressed it to me himself – "he felt as if the end of the world had indeed come".

The *Fever Hospital Medical Report for the Spring Assizes 1836* makes interesting reading. The number of cases treated since the previous Summer Assizes amounted to 384, of these 334 were discharged cured or relieved, 15 died and 35 remained under treatment. Low Typhus Fever was very prevalent, and it was thought that the pestilence could be checked by timely admission to hospital. It was further reported that from the effects of the infection Mr Murray the Apothecary had succumbed.

"In the Report made to you in the spring of 1835, it will be seen the cases admitted into hospital during the antecedent period from summer amounted to 173, the expenditure in the same period being £168-6-9$\frac{1}{2}$. For the corresponding period since the Summer Assizes 1835 nearly 400 cases have been under treatment and the expenditure has only increased by £56-17-8$\frac{1}{2}$!

In spite of such strict economy funds were exhausted and a special plea was being made to the Grand Jury for a second grant.

CLASSIFICATION OF DISEASES WAS AS FOLLOWS:

	ADMITTED	DIED		ADMITTED	DIED
FEVER:	368	11	INFLAMMATION OF THE BRAIN	1	1
SCARLET FEVER	6	1	OPHTHALMIC	1	0
DROPSY	2	1	DISEASE OF STOMACH	1	0
CONSUMPTION	1	1	JAUNDICE	1	0
SMALL POX	2	0	RHEUMATISM	1	0

Of a total of 384 patients admitted 15 died.

EXPENDITURE IN HOSPITAL SINCE SUMMER ASSIZES, 1835.

				£. s. d.
MEAT	.. 1289 lbs. at sundry prices	...	...	20-13 -7
BREAD	.. 1379 lbs. at do.	...	...	9-7- 6$^{1}/_{2}$
POTATOES	.. 251 pecks, at do.	...	...	11-10- 8
OATMEAL	.. 262 pecks, at do.	...		12- 6- 8
OATMEAL SEEDS	257 pecks, at do.	...		6-17-2$^{1}/_{2}$
NEWMILK	.. 7990 quarts at 1d. per quart	...		33- 5-10
BUTTERMILK	5798 quarts at sundry prices	...		11-17-11
SUGAR	.. 17$^{1}/_{4}$ stone, at do.	...	...	6-17- 7
BARLEY	.. 8$^{1}/_{2}$ stone, at 4s. per stone	...		1-14- 0
WINE	.. 52 bottles, at 2s. 8d. per bottle			6-18- 8
VINEGAR	.. 62 quarts, at 10d. per quart	...		2-11- 8
SOAP	.. 18 stone, at sundry prices	...		3- 1- 6
CANDLES	.. 208 lbs. at do.	...		4-18- 0
COALS	.. 19 tons, at do.	......		11-12- 0
STRAW	.. 39 cwt., at do.	......		2- 7-5$^{1}/_{2}$
TURF	.. ..	...		4-14- 0

CONTINGENCIES, viz.: Repairs, Utensils, and various articles included under this head, too numerous to mention separately, amounting to 20- 6 11

Paid for BEDTICKS, SHEETING, & COUNTERPANES ...   7- 8 11

Paid for GLAZING, opening & repairing the SEWERS & ROOF OF HOSPITAL 4- 7 0

Paid WILLIAM HARCOURT, PLUMBER, for different repairs done to the Pump 4- 4-10

Paid for BOARDS AND MAKING OF 6 COFFINS   ...   1-13- 0

MRS. BOLTON'S BILL for Printing Report...   ...   2- 0- 0

STEWARD AND HOUSEKEEPER's half year's salary ...				21- 0- 0
TWO NURSES	do.	...	...	5-10-10
PAID AN ADDITIONAL NURSE	...	...	...	2- 4- 7
WASHERWOMAN	do.	...	...	2- 8- 0
KITCHEN MAID	do.	...	...	1- 0- 0
PORTER	do.	...	...	2- 8- 0
				£225- 6- 5

During the terrible fever epidemic that followed the famine of 1846, O'Rorke tells us that the Fever Hospital, tho' only originally intended for for fifty patients in 1846 and 1847 accommodated 165 patients in the hospital itself, and in makeshift sheds and other buildings.

Sept. 1846 – Sept. 1847 – 1231 patients.

Sept 1847 – Sept 1848 – 1340 patients.

These buildings were crowded to capacity, while scores of stricken unfortunate men and women might be seen lying on wads of straw along the road from Calry church to Ballinode, waiting their turn to be received into one of the roofed structures. This was followed by the Cholera edpidemic of 1849. On this occasion the Fever Hospital was turned into a Cholera Hospital. One hundred and sixty six persons contracted the desease, ninety eight of whom died. It was less severe than the Cholera epidemic of 1832.

From the 6th January 1847 to 30th March 1851 – 5331 patients were treated in the Fever Hospital. In 1849 Dr. Thomas Little fell victim of Cholera. Having been engaged before his death until a late hour attending sick calls, instead of returning home he drove to the hospital and prescribed for every patient in the house. This devotedness was to cost him his his life.

The medical men in charge of the Fever Hospital since 1822 were Drs. Irwin, Coyne, Knott,Homan, Lynn and Murray.

In 1903 Dr. Murray and Dr.P.M.Quinn successfully dealt with an epidemic of Typhus and Typhoid. Dr. Murray in treating the thyphus epidemic regarded sneezing as a good prognostic sign. Each morning he would knock on the hospital door with his stick and ask of the Matron how many patients had sneezed that morning and he based his report on the reply! He also wrote a treatise arguing that Pulmonary Tuberculosis was caused by the blossoms of the Hawthorn.

(Personal communication from Dr. Patrick Heraughty).

County Sligo Fever Hospital in March of 1917 advertised in the local papers for a Nurse Matron – replies were to be sent to the *Secretary's Office, Workhouse.*

"The Joint Committee of management of the County Sligo Fever Hospital will at their meeting to be held on Saturday 24th day of March 1917 receive and consider applications for a 'trained' nurse to act as Matron of the County Sligo Fever Hospital at a salary of £50 a year increasing by annual increments of £5 until a maximum of £60 a year is realised, with first class rations and apartments, and an allowance of £3 annually for uniform. Applications, accompanied by certificates in Fever Training, testimonials etc., will be received up to the hour of 12 o'clock on the above date.

A months notice on either side to terminate the engagement.

The person appointed will be required to conform strictly to the rules and regulations laid down by the committee of management, and to enter into a bond with two solvent sureties, in the sum of £100 for the due and faithful discharge of the duties."

In the early thirties Dr. Hugh McLaughlin was physician to the Infirmary and to the Fever Hospital. Dr. Tom Murphy was the last physician to the Fever Hospital. It was closed down in 1958 *(Sligo Champion)* and was used as a staff and medical residence until it was demolished in 1978 in preparation for the orthopaedic unit, which was built in the early eighties.

MARKIEVICZ HOUSE
Used as St. Patrick's Hospital Tuberculosis Santorium

Chapter 10: Other Nursing, Hospital and Residential Centres.

GARDEN HILL NURSING HOME

A small private Nursing Home existed on The Mall earlier this century, and Mr T. J. Graham, Consultant ENT Surgeon came from Dublin to operate there from time to time. Later a Mrs Fleming came to Rosehill in Maugheraboy in the early thirties. She in turn invited Dr. Stafford-Johnson from Dublin, another ENT Surgeon to operate at Rosehill. At that time the story prevailed that Dr. Stafford-Johnson's hands had been blessed by the Pope. He would carry out removal of tonsils and adenoids by the guillotine method and often gave the anaesthetic himself.

Garden Hill was the home of the Robinson family. Roger D. Robinson was a guardian of the Poor Law Union. The Mc Gettricks lived there when it came on the market in the mid-thirties. Mrs Fleming purchased it and moved her Private Nursing Home business there from Rosehill, which no longer stands. In spite of the fact that Dr. Charles McCarthy had undergone training and had commenced ear, nose and throat operations at Sligo Infirmary, Dr. Stafford-Johnson continued to operate for some time in Garden Hill. Dr Heraughty recalls giving an occasional anaesthetic.

In 1948 the Home was purchased by Surgeon Denis Boland. He established a modern operating theatre and provided an excellent service for private patients for many years. A considerable amount of midwifery was undertaken there by the General Practioners of Sligo. The first time streptomycin was used in Ireland intrathecally, was in Garden Hill, and involved a young girl with Tuberculous Meningitis. Dr. Martin Roddy procured the drug for Dr. Patrick Heraughty from Dr Dunne, brother of Dr. John Dunne, who was working in New York.

In 1957 the Home was acquired by the Sisters of St. Joseph of the Apparition. Mr Boland continued to operate at Garden Hill until recently. Dr Gus Mulligan, a private ENT Surgeon carried out operations there for several years. The General Practioners used the Nursing Home to treat their private patients. A great deal of maternity work was also carried out there. The Home itself has been largely replaced by a modern private hospital with excellent facilities staffed by caring Sisters and nurses. Sister Angela Frawley who is Reverend Mother at present, first came to Garden Hill in 1961.

NAZARETH HOUSE.

This house was built by Sr John Moffet as 'Marine View House' in 1803. It was sold to William Pollexfen, uncle of W.B. Yeats in 1850. He renamed it 'Merville House' (Villa by the Sea). In 1899 Merville House became the property of Edward Tighe, a merchant in Sligo and he in turn sold the residence to the Nazareth Sisters in 1910. In 1915 Architect William Byrne, and builders Hall & Co. of Dublin designed and built the first phase of Nazareth House as it stands today.

The Official Opening of the second phase took place on the 24th May 1956. At that time the Mother Superior with 15 Sisters cared for 150 children and 100 adults.

Nazareth House was established to provide a home for the aged and infirm, also to care for deserted and orphaned children. It is worthy of note that on the 15th January 1936 there was a recital by John Count McCormack at the Gaiety Cinema, Sligo in an effort to raise funds for the Home.

The Nazareth House Brass Band enriched the town and county of Sligo from the 30's to the 70's. For eighty two years the Nazareth Nuns cared for, and prepared for life over 2000 children. In 1992 the work of the Sisters of Nazareth for children was completed, and the Nursery closed in 1993.

Care for 145 elderly residents continues. Aged persons of both sexes receive the best of medical care and attention in their declining years, from a staff of dedicated sisters and nurses.

CREGG HOUSE

In December 1955 eleven members of the Sisters of La Sagesse came to Cregg House to establish a residential centre for mentally handicapped girls. Initially there were thirty three children under their care. In the words of Rev. Dr. Hanly, Bishop of Elphin, at the ceremony of the laying of the corner stone of the new Home and School – "Heretofore we met these afflicted ones in the Imbecile Ward of the Workhouse, or in the Mental Hospital, where notwithstanding the best efforts of those in charge, their life was a dreary one until a merciful death removed them from a world that had little welcome for them".

The new Home and School, designed by Bernard Rhatigan, Architect, were officially opened on the 8th July 1963, and the care for the mentally handicapped in the North West was radically transformed.

One of the original Sisters who came, Sister Gerard Clancy, still takes an active part in the running of the centre. As well as a school for the moderately mentally handicapped, there is an excellent training school for nurses.

Today, with a dedicated staff, mentally handicapped children and adults, of both sexes, receive receive the best of care and attention.

BALLYMOTE NURSING HOME

This Home was opened in the early fifties when a congregation of the Sisters of St. John of God came from Perth, Australia and established a Nursing Home. It contained a fully fitted operating theatre. It provided a great service for the people of south Sligo, and was used extensively by the local doctors for maternity cases. In the mid seventies the maternity ceased and though the congregation are still there it was taken over by the North Western Health Board for the care of the aged.

COUNTY HOME: ST. JOHN'S HOSPITAL 1965

Chapter 11: Description of Dispensaries in County Sligo

and an account of illness and living conditions of the poor at that time. [Poor Inquiry (1835)]

BALLYMOTE DISPENSARY *Dr. Joseph Lougheed M.R.C.S, (dispensing doctor).*

This dispensary was established in 1818. It covered nine parishes. There were three dispensaries at Collooney, Riverstown and Tubbercurry all within a radius of ten miles. The doctors salary was £50 a year. He attended Ballymote dispensary two days a week, and was available at his home every day of the year, or if required would visit the poor in their huts. He did not attend any other dispensary. He kept a register in which it was recorded that he had relieved 3,500 patients. The chief illnesses were dyspepsia, catarrh, chronic affections of the lungs, diseases of the bones and joints, cephalalgia and a gastrodyme. He felt that when people had the comforts of life they seldom required medicine.

Messrs Boileau George and Co. Bride, Street Dublin, were the druggists. His receipts were £122 and expenditure £120 in the year 1832. With funds so limited a more efficient means of financing the service was necessary. "The poor are absolutely in a most heart rending condition. I cannot fully describe the wretchedness of the poor."

In the course of another examination he gives some idea of conditions that prevailed amongst the poor. He stated that there were many cases of dyspepsia arising from bad food. He felt that good diet, lodging and clothing would have prevented the disease. He agreed that there was no decrease in the imbibing of alcohol. It was only lack of means that prevented the poor from drinking to excess. He argued that the constant use of potatoes promoted disease.

In his area the poor were covered only in rags; the food only potatoes; bedding a little straw on the ground and scarcely any covering. They had little or no furniture and had no comfort.

COLLOONEY DISPENSARY

This dispensary was established in 1832 for the relief of the destitute sick. There was no other dispensary or hospital within the district. Dr. Thomas Armstrong attended St. John's Dispensary in Sligo which had opened in 1831, on two days a week and Collooney on one day a week. His salary for Collooney and St. John's was £50, depending on the funds. The year before he was paid £31-10-0. He kept a register of cases, treatment and outcome. He had attended 1,900 persons and relieved them. The principal ailments were inflammatory diseases of the chest and abdomen, with fevers and dyspepsia. Persons who sought urgent attention but were not poor were treated but had to pay for the medicine. The dispensary was funded by "subscriptions and presentments from the county Sligo". He felt that this Dispensary was being run as efficiently as possible with the funds available.

Considering the conditions of the poor patients he reported he had "seen fever of a malignant kind from want of cleanliness and poor ventilation". He agreed that the diet of the poor consisted of potatoes. He wouldn't agree that there was excess use of alcohol in the district. He felt that they had little or none of the comforts of life.

DRUMCLIFFE DISPENSARY

Drumcliffe and Ahamlish dispensary were established in 1822. – Dr. J. Powell, Surgeon.

The Sligo Hospital was nearby, and also near Carney and Grange. The doctor resided in Sligo. There was no medical practitioner residing in the district. He attended the dispensary twice a week for a salary of £50 per annum. He was always available for accidents, fever and severe inflammatory conditions. In the previous three years 3,877 patients had attended the dispensary and he had visited 500 to 600 patients in their homes for accidents, fevers, inflammations, dropsy. He was inclined to give patients medicine more readily because of the distance from his residence in Sligo. Stanley and Co. were druggists for the dispensary, some medicine was obtained from Murray, Apothecary, Sligo.

The dispensary was funded by subscription, charity sermons, petty session fines, and presentments from the county of Sligo.

He gave evidence of the increase in disease from uncleanliness, damp, and very imperfect ventilation. In his area he had seen severe cases of illness brought about by bad food, such as indifferent salt fish. He also observed that convalescence was retarded by want of wholesome nourishment. The diet consisted of potatoes, very little milk, and indifferent salt fish. He felt that suppression of illicit distillation in the area was the reason for reduced alcohol consumption. He felt that the living conditions of the poor were very bad in all respects.

DROMORE WEST – *Dr. Travers Homan M.D.*

This dispensary was established in 1822. Dr. Homan resided in Sligo town and attended Sligo Fever Hospital daily. He attended the dispensary on two days a week, this was a distance of 12 miles from Sligo. There was a Resident Apothecary attached to the dispensary who visited the sick when required. Dr. Homan's salary was £46 per annum for the Fever Hospital, and £56 for the dispensary. He visited nearly 600 patients in their homes in the previous three years, apart from the visits of the Resident Apothecary. The diseases treated were injuries, accidents, inflammation and dropsy.

The receipts amounted to £130 per annum and expenditure nearly the same. The apothecary's salary was £26-6-7d. The dispensary was funded by subscription and presentments from the county. Dr. Homan was managing a very extensive district with such small funds to the best of his ability.

His observations on ill health were such that he felt that conditions of ill health arose from damp, filth and bad ventilation. He felt that convalecence of illness was delayed by lack of nourishment which he felt more preferable to medicine. The diet in his area was in the main the potato. He felt that the intake of spirits was in the decline "more from the want of means to procure it, than any moral improvement."

RIVERSTOWN DISPENSARY: *Dr. Thomas Burrows M.D.*

This dispensary was established in 1822 with the object of treating the sick poor. The dispensary was 10 miles from Dr Burrow's residence. He attended Riverstown dispensary once a week. For this he had a salary of £60, and attended the Sligo dispensary, for £50 per annum. He resided in Sligo. A register was kept and the patient's name was not removed until discharged cured. From June 1830 to June 1833, 1985 patients attended. The ailments generally were chronic. They included pyrexia, dyspeptic patients and injuries of all sorts.

The medicines were sent by a druggist, and were compounded by the attendant apothecary. Expenditure for the year 1832 was £107-14s-0, this included the salaries of doctor, apothecary and registrar. Medicine, house rent and sundries came to £26-12s-5. The dispensary was funded by private subscriptions and presentment from the county of Sligo. Further comments by Dr. Burrows are interesting. He considered that all fever and epidemics had their origin among the poor, the cause of this being their extreme poverty, and the filthy mode of living, which he felt would persist as long as superstition and ignorance ruled their minds and habits. He felt that many diseases were brought about by the want of proper food, and the effects of medicine would be aided by proper food.

He found that the diet of the poor consisted of coarse vegetables particularly potatoes used invariably with sour milk or salt fish. "There is no district in the Kingdom in which illicit distillation is carried out to a greater extent than that of Riverstown" due to a combination of the low price of grain, and the inefficiency of the excise laws in the area. Some of the people were naked, the clothes of the worst kind; the food the coarsest and scanty; bed and furniture bad and filthy; ventilation: none except what the door admitted. These people had absolutely no comfort".

SLIGO DISPENSARY: *Mr. J. Murray -Registrar and Apothecary.*

This dispensary had been established in the town for almost thirty years. It was attended by Dr. Irwin, who also attended the Coolaney dispensary. The Sligo dispensary was also attended by Dr. Burrows who also attended Riverstown.

Dr. Irwin attended the Fever Hospital every day and the Sligo dispensary on two days in the week. Patients were also visited at home if necessary. Each physician received £60 per annum for attendance at Sligo Dispensary. A Register was kept of all cases, and a Medical Register of diseases and treatment. In the previous three years 7,527 patients had been treated at Sligo dispensary. The ailments consisted of "the pyrexia, disorders which the labouring poor are subject to, pulmonary and visceral diseases, dyspeptic complaints, surgical cases, especially affections of the skin, and midwifery cases".

The medicines for the dispensary were procured from Messrs. Leslie, Druggists in Dublin, and compounded at the dispensary by the apothecary.

Receipts for the previous three years were £1,206-17-18$\frac{1}{2}$ while expenditure was £1,169-17-1$\frac{1}{2}$ – this included medicines, and surgical necessities such as trusses for the patients, salaries for the physicians, apothecary, porter and fuel and stationery.

Giving evidence the doctors and committee felt that typhus prevailed in the town very extensively when the food was dear, and of bad quality. The poor lived on the potato but often the crop failed or was bad, this was when disease occurred. In the town the use of spirits was a source of much evil, and at times was imbibed greatly in excess.

ST. JOHN'S DISPENSARY (SLIGO) *Dr. James Kenny, Surgeon; Dr. Thomas Armstrong, Physician.*

This dispensary under the care of Dr. James Kenny, senior physician and surgeon, and the apothecary, was opened on the 19th December 1831. The dispensary was open every day. The Medical Officers visited the sick poor in their homes, and attended the lying-in poor within the corporation as no hospital had yet been established for their relief. There was an Infirmary, a Fever Hospital and a Dispensary all within the parish of Calry.

Dr. Kenny only attended the St. John's dispensary, while Dr. Armstrong attended the St. John's and the Collooney dispensaries. The salary of the Medical Officers of St. John's was only £100 per annum. The principal days were Mondays and Thursdays.

They were obliged by the rules of the institution to attend the poor confined by illness at their own homes, and the lying-in women within the corporation, which was a mile all round the town. They often went three or four miles to visit the distressed on the recommendation of the subscribers.

A careful record was kept of the names, age, and residence of the patients, also the names and residence of the subscribers recommending them. Physicians books were also kept where the history of the disease, remedies given and the result given at the close – whether cured, relieved or died.

Between 19th June 1831 when it opened, and the 26th June 1833 *not including two months of cholera*, there were 2,625 patients of whom 2,306 were cured or relieved; 16 died, while 303 remained in attendance. Of the above number 576 sick poor were visited in their homes, including 23 "laborious midwifery" cases. The medicines were obtained, by an order from the treasurer Rev. James Dotdevy, from the Dublin druggists Pollock and Company, Capel St., and Leslie and Co. Brides St. The receipts for 1833 were £199-3s-3d and expenditure was £242-8-2.

It was felt that the present funds were inadequate. However if constant employment could be adopted in order to procure good food and good clothing, this would reduce the need for medicine.

It was felt that fevers of a particular type were prevalent "so as to render the pulmonary system, the principal seat of disease, owing a great measure to the inclemency of the seasons, exposure to wet and cold and bad clothing". They felt that consumption of alcohol was on the decrease "for want of means not from any influence of the Temperance Society".

TUBBERCURRY DISPENSARY: *Dr. William Powell M.D. L.R.C.S.E.*

This dispensary was established on the 16th July 1833 to give advice and medicine to the sick poor. If required by a subscriber the doctor was obliged to attend patients in their houses, such individuals rendered incapable by disease or injury from coming to the Institution. Dr. Powell attended only one dispensary and resided there in the district. His salary was £40 a year and he devoted one day a week exclusively to the poor. Like his colleagues he kept a record of each patient, name, age, disease, treatment and final outcome. From the 29th August 1833, the first day it opened, until 12th December 1833 – 200 patients had attended, 113 had been cured, 24 relieved, 3 died and 60 remained under treatment.

The medicines were purchased from a Dublin druggist and the debt liquidated by the Grand Jury donation. One half of the upkeep of the dispensary was obtained by subscription and the other half by a grant from the Sligo Grand Jury. It was felt that no further change could be made that would bring more relief to the poor.

When Dr. Powell was interviewed further, he felt that in

Ireland generally, fevers were of a mixed kind. The fevers were inflammatory at the commencement but toward their conclusion "the typhoid symptoms preponderate. The cases of fever I have seen here among the poor clearly assumed a typhoid character. Sufficient cause may be found in the want of proper sustenance, cleanliness and ventilation". He felt that the mere restoration of sustenance itself would not be sufficient without the intervention of the healing art. A bad potato tended to derange the healthy action of the digestive organs. He came to the conclusion the physiologists felt, that the most appropriate diet for man should be partly animal, partly vegetable. Again he commented on the apalling living conditions – the clothes, bedding, food and furniture all being of the worst and coarsest.

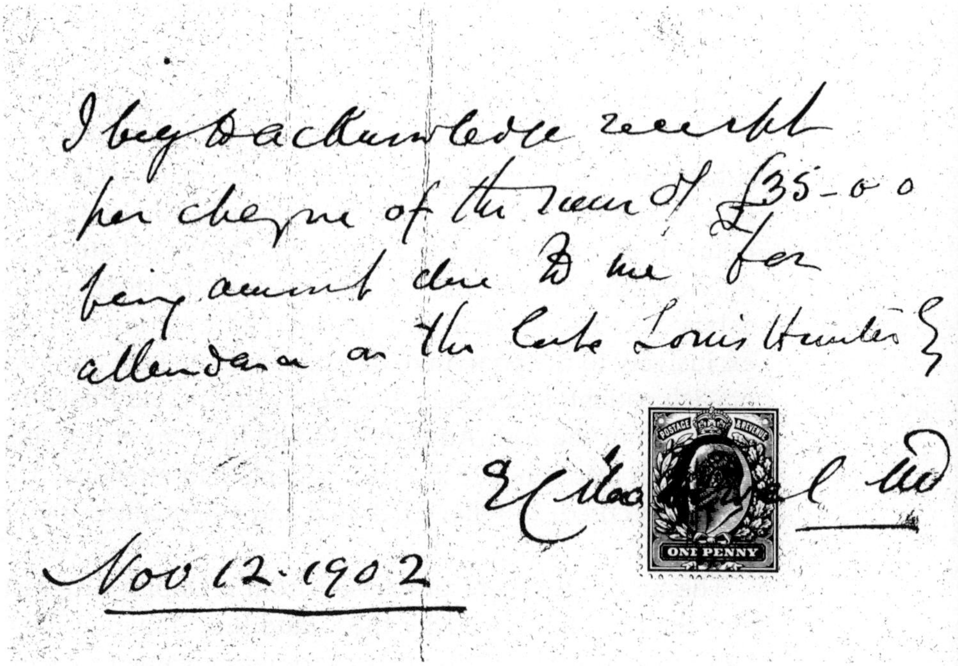

I beg to acknowledge receipt per cheque of the sum of £35-0-0 being amount due to me for attendance on the late Louis Hunter

Nov 12. 1902

Retail Quantities at Wholesale Prices for **Cash only.**

TELEGRAMS—"DENNING, SLIGO."

ESTD. 1815.

Sligo 2 . 8 / 1902 18

The Late Lewis W. Hunter

Sligo

BOUGHT AT DENNING'S DRUG HALL.

Horse & Cattle Medicines.

DRUGS, PATENT MEDICINES, PERFUMERY, HAIR, NAIL & TOOTH BRUSHES, COMBS, SPONGES,
TOILET REQUISITES OF THE BEST QUALITY & AT REASONABLE PRICES.

Prescriptions and Family Receipts carefully compounded.

PARCELS POST DEPARTMENT.

*All orders to this department must be accompanied by a Cash
Remittance to cover Price of Goods and Postage. If too much is
sent, the balance will be returned. In no case will the Goods be
forwarded until payment has been received.*

In your reply quote this No

3 4

	1902					
June	23	To 1 box Frog in throat			7	½
July	26	. 1 bot Cresoline			1	..
		. 2 . Carbolic acid			2	.
		, 1 roll absorbent wool			3	.
		G____ ____ ue			2	6
				£	9	2

No. **2712** Sligo, 12. 11. 1902

Received on account of

Arthur Denning & Sons,
   Larkhill Mineral Water Factory,

the sum of £   9/2

With thanks

No receipt valid unless given on one of these printed forms.

amount *by return with this statement.*
Sligo, *to C. J. Denning & Co.*

We are the Publishers of Denning's Medical Dictionary and Complete Price List, which shall be sent free on
demand. Contains a great deal of useful information—*see* PRESS NOTICES.

Dr. P .M. Quinn.

Dr. James Gordon Flannery.

Chapter 12: **An Account of certain Sligo Doctors.**

DR. HENRY BELL: Physician and Surgeon died of Cholera 1832.

DR. HENRY IRWIN served in the army in the Peninsular War and also at Waterloo. He became Deputy General of hospitals before his appointment in 1817 as Surgeon to the Sligo militia. He subsequently was physician at the county Fever Hospital. He practised at Stephen St. and died April 1836. He published an account of the Cholera Epidemic – August and September 1832.

DR. EDWARD KNOTT was appointed Physician to the Fever Hospital in 1836 in succession to Dr. Irwin. He was a fellow of the Royal College of Surgeons in Ireland. He was appointed Physician to Sligo Workhouse in 1841. In 1849 he was appointed Surgeon to the County Infirmary in succession to Dr. Little. In 1852 he was appointed Physician to Mayo County Infirmary.

DR. THOMAS LITTLE: Surgeon to Sligo County Infirmary for seventeen years contracted Cholera in the course of his duties. He died at his residence at Old Market St., on the 14th August 1849 aged 66 years.

DR. WILLIAM S. LITTLE, M.D. son of Dr. Thomas Little became surgeon at the County Infirmary. In 1864 he was elected a Town and Harbour Commissioner. He was also Physician to the Asylum. He died at his residence Caldwell Place, Chapel St., December 1876 aged 65 years. He was buried at St. John's. In an obituary in the *Sligo Independent* on 9th December 1876 the death of William Swayne Little was recorded as well as that of his father. Of Dr. Thomas it said *"His name is still cherished in Sligo and a tribute to his memory is placed in the hall of the County Infirmary the scene of*

his many victories over diseases of all kinds."

Of William it states *"Besides the Post of Surgeon to the County Infirmary and Jail (both appointments being joined by Act of Parliament) he held the office of consulting and visiting physician to the District Lunatic Asylum."*

DR. EDWARD LYNN died in May 1873 at his residence in Stephen St. The event was recorded in the *Sligo Independent*. *"He was a Bachelor of Arts and a Bachelor of Medicine in connection with Trinity College, and a licentiate and Fellow of the Royal College of Surgeons, Ireland, also a licentiate and Fellow in midwifery. He succeeded Dr Homan as medical attendant at the County Fever Hospital, and for many years he discharged the duties of surgeon to the hospital in the County Jail. He was also one of the Medical Officers of Sligo Dispensary. He died at the age of 65 years"*.

DR. R. H. WOOD J.P. His death was recorded on March 20th 1888 (*Sligo Independent*) *"The venerable doctor who had more than covered the allotted span of years had been ailing for some time"*.

He was born in Skreen and first started practice in Ratcliffe St., and later went to Wine St., Sligo. *"While he had been gathered to his father like a sheaf of wheat fully ripe, it should at the same time be said that all through a blameless life he was wearing the light yoke of that Lord of Love, who stilled the stormy sea of Galilee"*.

DR. ARCHIBALD ARMSTRONG: *O'Rorke's History of Sligo* states that he practised in Sligo in the early nineteenth century. He was a man of high standing in his profession. He had three sons, Archibald, Tom and William who were similarly distinguished – Archibald in Sligo and Tom and William in Collooney where they occupied successively the position of Medical Officer of the district. William succeeding to the post on the death of Tom. Dr. William of Collooney left after him two sons and a daughter.

William the elder of the two sons, who like his father and uncle was Medical Officer of the Collooney Dispensary district, was cut off in 1875 in the prime of his life, and in the opening of what promised to be a brilliant career, by a malignant fever caught while attending at the bedside of a patient. Dr. William Armstrong is buried in the graveyard attached to the Protestant Church of Collooney and the following epitaph is inscribed on his tomb. *"William Armstrong. Medical Officer of the Collooney Dispensary District died on Friday April 16th 1875 of fever, taken in the faithful and fearless discharge of his duty, aged 36 years"*. The widow of Dr. William Armstrong though not a nurse was later appointed Matron of the Lunatic Asylum.

The McMunn family seem to have been quite a dynasty to judge from extracts of the Medical Directory of 1862.

McMUNN, JAMES, EASKY, Dromore West, Co. Sligo. M.D. and C.M. Glasgow 1846. L.A.H. Dub 1840 L.M. Dub 1840. Medical Officer, Dromore West Workhouse and Easky Dis. and Constabulary.

McMUNN, JOHN. Res. Phys. and Superintendent Dist. Lunatic Asylum, Sligo, M.D. Glasgow 1836. L.F.P.S. Glasgow 1852. L.A.H. Dub. 1838. L.M. Dub. Rot. Hosp. 1837. Late Medical Officer Union Workhouse. Late Physician, Board of Health Fever Hospital. Author of *'Annual Reports of Sligo District Asylum'*.

McMUNN, ROBERT. Skreen, Collooney, Co. Sligo. M.D. and C.M. Glasgow 1853, L.M. Coombe Hospital 1850 Medical Officer, Skreen Dispensary District and Medical Attendant, Chapelfield Constabulary.

McMUNN, SAMUEL, The Castle, Ballymote, Co. Sligo. L.R.C.S.I. 1854. L.M. Rotunda Hospital, Dublin. Medical Officer, Gurteen Dispensary District, Surgeon, Clogher and Mullaghroe Constabulary.

DR. EFFINGHAM CARROLL MacDOWEL, one of the most remarkable doctors in Sligo was appointed Physician and Surgeon to Sligo Infirmary in 1877, a post that he occupied for forty six years until his death in 1924, at the age of 73 years. He was also consultant physician to the District Lunatic Asylum. Such was his fame that patients in the last stages of consumption would say "I'd be all right if I could only get a ticket to the Infirmary". Nobody ever knew him to ask the poor for money. One son, Surgeon Lieut. Comdt. Frank Mac Dowel married Miss Winifred Hosie of Castledargan. His elder daughter married Major Perceval of Templehouse. Anti Tuberculosis campaigns, District Nursing and better housing all had his support. *(Sligo Champion, March 1924.)*. Later in an obituary notice for his wife Mrs Mary MacDowel it described her husband: "for years her late husband E.C.MacDowel M.D. FRSI. who died in 1924 was well known in Sligo where he practised for 46 years and had the post of surgeon to the County Infirmary for that period". *(Sligo Champion 23/9/1950)*.

In a separate account of his career it was stated that he filled the important position as surgeon to the Infirmary from 1877 when he was first appointed "until a short time since, when it seemed good to the powers that be to retire him". He had reached the limit of three score years and ten.

Dr. MacDowel's staff at the County Infirmary, consisted of an apothecary, a treasurer, a matron a house steward, three nurses, two wards maids, two laundry maids, a cook and a night nurse. Before a Joint Committee of management in march 1917 Dr. MacDowel applied for an increase in his house allowance. He stated that he was forty one years Surgeon to the County Infimary and he was allowed £80 for house, coal etc. He had never before applied for an increase When the Tuberculosis Scheme came into operation he did any surgical work necessary gratuitously, while other doctors were receiving fees. The Chairman and members paid a fitting tribute to the manner in which Dr. MacDowel carried out his duties, and he was unanimously granted an increase of £40. Dr. MacDowel briefly returned thanks.

(Sligo Independent, March 24th 1917.

His sterling qualities were described in an obituary published on March 8th 1924 in the Lancet. *"Dr. Effingham Carroll Mac Dowel, Surgeon to the County Sligo Infirmary, died on February 23rd, 1924 after a protracted illness at the age of 73. Born in 1851 he was the eldest son of the late Dr Benjamin MacDowel, Professor of Anatomy and Chirugery in Trinity College, Dublin. He was educated at Trinity College where he graduated Bachelor of Arts, had a distinguished student career both in Arts and in Medicine, and later went to Oxford University as Radcliffe Medical Scholar. Having obtained his A.B. he took the M.D. Dub. in 1875. While still a young man he was elected Surgeon to the County Sligo Infirmary where he continued to perform the duties of that post for some 46 years, until a few months ago. He was also Visiting Physician to the Sligo and Leitrim District Lunatic Asylum. In 1883 he became a Fellow of the Royal College of Physicians of Ireland, a qualification that was exceptional among country practitioners in Ireland. In the year 1907-08 he was President of the Irish Medical Association, which in that year held its annual meeting in Sligo. Dr. MacDowel was one of the leading practitioners in the West of Ireland, and for many years he enjoyed a large consulting practice.*

He was a man of much culture, a sound diagnostician, possessed of considerable operative skill, and he took much pains to keep abreast of the advances in medical and surgical knowledge. His health had suffered since he lost his eldest son in the war. The next surviving son Dr. F.L.H. McDowel, is a surgeon in the navy."

His son Benjamin Louis had been killed in France in 1915 while cutting barbed wire before the enemy trenches. *(Irish Times 25/4/1924.*

I understand that a plaque was erected to the memory of Dr. Effingham MacDowel in the County Sligo Infirmary shortly after his death.

FLANNERY, JAMES GORDON, was appointed to Tubbercurry Dispensary District in 1878. He was said to have been of weak build. On occasions when he had to apply the forceps for a domiciliary delivery he would have the man of the house pull him from behind to assist traction!

He was a man who did not agree with Lister's theories on asepsis. On one occasion he was called to a house following a stabbing incident. A section of bowel was protruding. Taking out a special pocket knife he enlarged the wound – replaced the bowel with his fingers and applied a few stitches. The man made an uneventful recovery without infection or fever.

He achieved considerable fame in the treatment of sciatica. He would use Corrigan's button suitably heated with a methylated spirits bunsen burner. He would apply the heated button along the path of the sciatic nerve until it blistered the skin. He died in 1920.

FLANNERY JOHN, A., his son was appointed to Tubbercurry Dispensary, in 1911. He died 1977. Dr. Eveline Flannery, his wife qualified in 1914. Their son Dr. Sean Flannery succeeded as dispensary doctor in Tubbercurry in 1962.

JOHN LAIRD: Practised at 1 Wine St. In 1912 he wrote a small book *'Notes on the Treatment of Tuberculosis'*. The book was printed in Bristol. The purpose of the book was to put before the medical profession his experience in treating this disease over many years. He used a mixture of Iodine, Sodium Benzoate, Arsenic, Tincture of Pulsatilla' which cleared the respiratory passages, and tincture of Baptista. He found that a mixture of all these preparations gave great results in the treatment of Tuberculosis in its various forms.

He dealt at length with the use of Calcium Salts as a preventative of the disease. He claimed that workers in Lime Kilns showed great freedom from the disease. He was aware of the dangers of getting Tuberculosis from cows milk and recommended the importation of herds of goats whose milk would be free of the disease. He deplored the practice of excision of tuberculosis glands and claimed it would be unnecessary if the mixture he recommended was used with Calcium Salts. He welcomed "the diagnostic powers of Radiography", recently introduced, in the fight to combat this disease.

DR. PATRICK BURKE, was Tuberculosis Officer for County Sligo. He qualified in 1912, and was appointed to his office in 1914, and he married in 1916. The roads were very bad and tubed tyres were necessary. In his early days he was the envy of the profession with his chauffeur driven car. The chauffeur was always in livery. Each Thursday, Dr. Burke held a clinic in a room on the ground floor at the infirmary and visited patients in their homes. In 1931 Cloonamahon, beyond Collooney, became the Tuberculosis sanitorium. This closed in December 1943. During the war some of the patients were transferred to the County Home. In January 1944 Markievicz House became St. Patrick's Hospital for Tuberculosis in Sligo. It closed down in 1959. When Dr Michael Kirby was appointed Medical Officer of health in 1930 Dr Burke was retained as Tuberculosis Officer with the status of Assistant Co. Medical Officer of health. Cloonamahon later became a residential centre for the mentally handicapped.

DR. P. M. QUINN came to Sligo on the outbreak of the Typhus epidemic to assist Dr Murray. He was a Physician to the Fever Hospital and Assistant Surgeon at Sligo Infirmary to Dr. MacDowel. Out of 14 patients in that epidemic in 1903 there were only four deaths. In 1913 as Coroner he held a widely publicised inquest surrounding the death of a Patrick Dunbar, alleged strike breaker at Sligo quays. As a result the coroner exhorted Sligo Co. Council to provide an ambulance to convey patients to hospital from all parts of the county. He was succeeded by his son Dr. Thomas Quinn, Opthalmologist, and later by his grandson Dr. Patrick Quinn in General Practice.

DR. MARTIN BRENNAN, qualified in Dublin in 1927 having been born in 1901. He was appointed Medical Officer for Aclare and was enormously popular. On the occasion of his marriage his friends presented him with "a motor car and an address." *(Irish Independent)*

He was involved in the War of the Black and Tans, and later Commandant of the 4th brigade during the Civil War.

He was said to have been a fearless soldier "even when under sentence of death he never wavered." He went into politics and and was elected a Dáil deputy. He was later appointed film censor. He died in 1956.

DR. BRIAN CRICHTON was in General Practice at his family home at Carrowgarry, Beltra, (1933-1950). He studied Paediatrics in Vienna, and attended Great Ormond Street hospital in London. He returned to Dublin and was one of the first Paediatricians in Dublin, attached to the Children's Hospital Harcourt St., and Temple St. At the time of his father's death he moved back to the family home and combined farming and medicine. He published a book on *Infant Feeding* and his advice was much sought after. His great grandfather Sir Alexander Crichton was responsible, by his publications, for many of the changes in the treatment of the mentally handicapped. With other doctors he served the Czar of Russia and reorganised the medical services in St. Petersburg.

DR. PATRICK FLANAGAN, late of 1 Wine St., practised in Sligo in the nineteen twenties. He was Medical Officer of the County Home having previously been Dispensary Doctor at Carney. He frequently got calls to the Carney area. On one occasion he visited a man with Bronchitis and arranged to call back after two days. The following day when examining a patient at Wine St. he couldn't find his thermometer. He created a terrible fuss but eventually had to go out and buy one. The next day when he visited his patient in Carney he was astonished to see one of the patient's arms all tied up. On enquiring what was wrong he was reassured that all was well but this was the only way he could "keep that little thing where the doctor had put it".

DR. THOMAS GRAY was Dispensary Doctor in Cliffoney in 1916, but eventually left to practise in Mohill. He was father of Mrs Gladys Monahan of Ballincar.

DR. CHARLES McCARTHY succeeded Dr. Mac Dowel as County Surgeon reportedly in 1923. He was said to have been appointed by an Anti Treaty/Labour County Council majority. His opponent for the post was Dr. Cullen, brother-in-law of Dr. Michael Martin of Cashelgarron. The story goes that he received confirmation of his appointment in Irish and he brought the letter to a teacher friend to translate. The letter is said to have gone on to congratulate him in having done well at his Irish exam!

He was a native of Tralee. He graduated in 1916, with first place and first class honours. He was in General Practice in Swinford, having failed to obtain a surgical post at the Mater Hospital, when the vacancy in Sligo arose. He served the people of Sligo well, and was known for his great sense of humour. Everybody knew 'Charlie McCarthy'. He was excluded from the planning of the hospital that was built in the early forties and subsequently it was he who pointed out the day before the hospital was to be officially opened that some one had forgotton to wire the building for electricity! Evidence of this omission was later seen in the walls of the building where the plaster had to be disturbed to correct the mistake. He died in 1975.

DR. MICHAEL KIRBY. In 1869 a meeting of the Medical Officers in Sligo & Leitrim presented a Memorial on the subject of Public Health administration to the Lord Lieutenant. It was not until 1930 that Dr. Michael Kirby was appointed to his post in Sligo, and he was the first Medical Officer of Health for Co. Sligo. He held this position with distinction and died in office in 1964. His wife Sheelah was a local historian and wrote a book '*The Yeats Country*'.

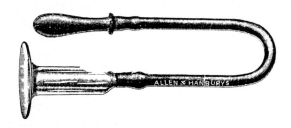

DR. JOHN MORAN: The Moran family lived in Terratick House in Ballintogher, Co. Sligo. John was born in 1892. He qualified in 1914 and served in the British army. He landed on a beach head in the Dardanelles in 1916. He returned to Carney dispensary, and became politically involved, assisting the First Aid Training for Sinn Féin. He became Coroner for North Sligo in 1943 and held that post until he died in 1959.

His brother EDWARD MORAN interestingly left Maynooth College, where he was a class-mate of the late Bishop Hanly of Elphin, to assume second in command of the old I.R.A. (south Sligo). He later qualified as a doctor, and was Dispensary Doctor in Drumkeerin, Co. Leitrim until his death in 1938.

DR. KATHLEEN MORAN, a sister was also born in Tarratick House in 1899. She was said to have been the first woman Dispensary Doctor appointed in Ireland. She died in Dublin in 1995.

DR. DESMOND MORAN, a nephew of the above is now Coroner of North Sligo, and is in General Practice.

DR. THOMAS McDONAGH was born in Ballymote 1902. He qualified in U.C.G. and returned from England to become Dispensary Doctor for Coolaney. He died in 1976. His brother Dr. Harry McDonagh was also born in Ballymote. He practised in Sligo for some time after qualifying, then he went to Ballymote and Geevagh. Eventually he left to become Prison Doctor to Portlaoise Gaol. He died in 1992. Dr Brian McDonagh is son of Thomas McDonagh and is Paediatrician at Sligo General Hospital.

DR. PATRICK O' HART was Dispensary Doctor in Ballymote for forty two years. He was present during the Great Flu Epidemic after World War I. He was succeeded by his son Dr. Frank O'Hart, who in turn spent twenty three years as the Ballymote Dispensary Doctor. Frank died in 1983.

Chapter 13: Renowned Doctors of Sligo Origin.

DR. CHARLES ALEXANDER McMUNN was the son of Dr. James McMunn born at Seafield Co. Sligo 1852. He became Honorary Consultant Physician to the General Hospital, Wolverhampton. He published the *'The Clinical Chemistry of Urine'*. He discovered Uro-Haematoporphyrin. His name has been identified with the use of the spectroscope and his work on pigments.

DR. CHARLES BENSON was born in Sligo in 1797. He was elected Professor of medicine in 1836 and was for many years physician to the City of Dublin Hospital. He played a large part in the foundation of the Medical Benevolent Fund Society. He was Professor of Medicine at the Royal College of Surgeons for thirty six years until his eyesight failed him with glaucoma.

DR. BRYAN HIGGINS: Physician and Chemist. Born in Sligo about 1737. He commenced Practice in London and opened a school in Practical Chemistry in Greek St. He visited Russia on the invitation of Catherine the Great. He published many papers. When the House of Assembly, Jamaica formed a committee for the improvement of the manufacture of Muscovado sugar and rum, Higgins was engaged to assist them. He died in 1820.

WILLIAM HIGGINS was born in County Sligo, nephew of Dr. Bryan Higgins. In June 1806 he was elected F.R.S. but never presented himself for admission. He became Professor of Chemistry to the Royal Dublin Society. He died in 1855.

The Dublin *Quarterly Journal of Medical Science* Vol 8 (1849) highlighted the work of Bryan and later William

Higgins. William was at first appointed chemist to the Apothecaries company of Ireland at a salary of £200 a year, apartments, coals and candles. The Law of Multiple Proportions was discovered by William Higgins which related to the proportions in which gases combine. For this he has been given credit.

PROFESSOR ROBERT JAMES ROWLETTE was born in Sligo in 1873 and was an uncle of the Rowlette family late of Wine St. He graduated in Trinity in 1898. It was said that when he qualified his family wished him to take Carney dispensary but instead he signed up for two years working on a ship. He was appointed physician to Jervis St. Hospital and later to Mercers Hospital. He was a man of great wisdom and sound judgement. He was President of the Irish Medical Association in 1932. In 1936 he was elected Editor of the *'Journal of the Irish Free State Medical Union'*. He was a member of the Dáil and later of the Senate. In 1926 he was elected King's Professor of Modern Medicine and Pharmacology in Trinity College Medical School. In 1940 he became president of the Royal Academy of Medicine. He helped establish the Medical Registration Council in 1927. *(Journal of I.M.A. Nov. 1944).*

In his early years 1904-1909 he lectured in Queens College Galway, teaching Pathology. He visited Galway twice weekly by rail taking specimens with him in the rail van. One day the R.I.C. were waiting for him on the platform – a curious porter had peeked at the specimens in the van and thought he had a murder on his hands!

During his life he worked tirelessly to try and improve the Dispensary System in Ireland. *The Irish Times*, Monday 16th October 1944 recording his death observed, that his election to the Dáil was noted for the fact that he was the first member who had not been required to subscribe to the statutory declaration that he would take the oath of allegiance to the King, as this had just been removed from the constitution. He was President of the Irish amateur Athletics Association from 1908 to 1920. He was described as a great Sligo man and a contemporary of Yeats. Though he held a prominent position in medical circles for a great number of years he never owned a motor car.

DR. JAMES T. GALLAGHER (1855-1936) Born in County Sligo and educated at Queens College, Galway and emigrated to the U.S. in 1880. He practised in Boston and was a distinguished physician, patriot and poet.

> " *Rolling down to Sligo on a summer day*
> *Snowy hawthorn hedges smiling all the way*
> *The road is perfumed ribbon winding up and down*
> *A little road to paradise leads to my native town.*"

DR. THOMAS FERRAR. This is an intriguing tale. The Belfast Academical Institution predated Queens University in Belfast. C.A. Cameron (*History of the Royal College of Surgeons in Ireland* and of the *Irish Schools of Medicine* 2nd edition, 1916) described the medical school of the Royal Belfast Academical Institution in 1835. Thomas Ferrar M.D is listed as Professor of Surgery. He received his B.A. at T.C.D. (1826) and MB at T.C.D. (1829). It is not certain where he obtained his M.D. He is listed in the *Medical Directory* of Croly, 1843 (p.21) and again in 1846 (p.9). The *Irish Medical Directory* started in 1852, but he was not mentioned in that or subsequent directories.

In the fourteen years of this Medical School 1835-1849 the school had 400 students. Dr. John McDonnell was appointed first Professor of Surgery but never gave a lecture. He resigned and took up a post at the Richmond Hospital, Dublin. He was replaced by Dr. Thomas Ferrar. He never turned up, being concerned with "a defective element in the constitution of the school", ie the then non recognition by the University of London, and the failure of the College Hospital to which he offered his services gratuitously.

On the 2nd November at 2am he wrote to the Royal Belfast Academical Institution from Castle St. at Sligo explaining that he could not take up the R.B.A.I. post "because urgent and inevitable business occurring within the last ten hours renders my absence from my present post altogether out of my own power". The letter was stamped "Sligo, 2nd November 1836, and Enniskillen 2nd. Nov., 1836, and was received at the Royal Belfast Academical Institution on the same day! He was discharged without ever giving a lecture.

What was the urgent and inevitable business? He wrote again to the R.B.A.I. on 19th November. " I would gladly become resident surgeon of the new College Hospital gratuitously"!

What was his ultimate fate and did he work in Sligo? However in the *Belfast Newsletter* on the 9th June 1837 there appeared the following obituary notice. " At Sligo. Thomas Ferrar M.D. on 2nd June 1837. Second surviving son of the late W.H. Ferrar, Belfast". This notice of his death appeared in spite of the fact that Croly had recorded him in the Medical Directories for 1843 and 1846!

(Sir Peter Froggatt – Personal Communication)

DR. JEREMY SWAN was born in Sligo in 1922. Both his parents were doctors practising in Sligo. He published a monogram on *'Sympathetic Control of Human Blood Vessels'* with Dr. Henry Bancroft at St. Thomas' Hospital, London. A Cardiologist of note he went to the United States where with Dr William Ganz he developed the Swan-Ganz catheter revolutionising the measurement of cardiac function, bringing haemodynamic monitoring to Coronary Care and Intensive Care Units throughout the world

(Irish Medical Times).

DR. CHARLES JOHNSTON was one time Professor of Midwifery at the Royal College of Surgeons in Ireland. It was known that he had a Sligo mother.

DR. CHARLES HAWKES TODD was President of the Royal College of Surgeons in Ireland in the year 1821. He was born in Sligo in 1782 where his father was in practice. His mother was a distant relation of Oliver Goldsmith.

DR. CHARLES BENSON was President in 1854-5. He was born in Sligo in 1797. Probably as a direct result of his Sligo connection he was indentured to Dr. Todd in the year 1815.

Out of interest I include a list of Sligo Doctors who, I recall, left Sligo before 1960 after qualifying:

BURKE, COLEMAN: Physician, Michigan, U.S.A.

BUTLER, GORDON: Canadian Army.

BUTLER, KENNETH: Physician, Canada.

FARRELL, T.C.: late Minister for Health, Newfoundland.

FLANAGAN, BRENDAN: OB/Gynaecologist, California, U.S.A.

HANNON DR.: Anaesthetist, Richmond Hospital.

HARAN, MICHAEL: North America.

HENRY, MICHAEL: Anaesthesiologist, Portland, Oregon, U.S.A. Brother of the Author.

HIGGINS, DERMOT Australia.

LIVESAY B. (Nee Foley) England. Retired to Sligo.

KANE, KATHLEEN & SISTER: Both doctors left Sligo after qualifying.

MALONEY, PADRAIG: Physician, California, U.S.A.

MULLEN, PETER: England.

MULLIGAN, JACK: Psychiatrist, U.S. Army.

McCARTHY, DONAL: Portlaoise, Co. Physician, son of Surgeon Charlie McCarthy.

Mac SEARRAIG EAMONN: Newcastle, England, retired to Sligo.

PARKER, DESMOND: Newcastle, Limerick.

RAFTERY, HUGH: Anaesthetist, Dublin.

RAFTERY, MICHAEL: Physician, Michigan U.S.A.

SCALLEN, MARGARET (Nee Raftery) Yorkshire, England.

SWAN, DAVID: England, son of Dr. Harold Swan and brother of Dr. Jeremy Swan.

Dr. Charles McCarthy

Dr. Tom Murphy,
Sligo Fever Hospital.

Chapter 14: Sligo Doctors in the Press.

Included in this book is a story which I feel is worthy of being presented verbatim. It appeared in the *Sligo Chronicle* on Saturday July 17th, 1855 and demonstrates that journalists in those days were capable of unearthing an intriguing story and presenting it in a fascinating manner.

THE LATE DR. CARTER.

"On Christmas day this gentleman lay dead in his large house in Wine St. He was, in many respects, a remarkable man. He possessed mental powers of a high order, and, by long and successful practice as a physician, had amassed a considerable fortune. He outlived nearly all his contemporaries, having achieved the patriarchal age of 86. Time dealt gently with the old man, as he retained his mental faculties, unimpaired, nearly to the last moment of his life, and possessed physical strength enjoyed by but few octogenarians. He was a widower, and childless; neither brother nor sister, nor their descendants, and for a few years before his death, lived almost completely retired in his great roomy house. His death was somewhat sudden and he departed this life without making a will –at least none was found in the house after the funeral, when a grand search was made in the drawers, and desks, and other repositories.

The search was conducted by strangers, who carefully sealed up the securities for money and other valuable property that they discovered, in order to preserve them for next of kin. The scene was a strange one – a crowd, many of whom had never crossed the threshold before, ransacked the house and scrutinised the contents of the Sanctum Sanctorum – the old fashioned chest of drawers in the bedroom, where the bonds, and mortgages and receipts for stock were carefully deposited!! It was a striking illustration of the words that had been read in the morning over the late owner of the wealth "man walketh in a vain shadow, and disquieteth himself in vain; he heapeth up riches and cannot tell who shall gather them."

When it was ascertained that no will had been made the next of kin appeared in crowds – a regiment – an army ready to rush upon the premises. It soon became manifest that a battle among the rival claimants was inevitable. African travellers tell us that when a large animal dies in the desert, specks soon appear on the horizon, which expand and approach until the air is darkened and the desert resounds with the flapping of wings and horrid cries – it is the vultures rushing to tear away a meal. The unlooked for crowds who appear when a rich man dies intestate, are not very unlike the vultures, whether as regards their numbers or rapacity. The trial which terminated on Wednesday was contested between two classes of claimants – first cousins, and first once removed. The question to be decided was whether Sir John Benson, the plaintiff was the first cousin of the deceased. This affected the entire claim of the defendants, because if the plaintiff established his kindred, none of those standing in a lower degree would be entitled under the Statute of Distributions, to any share of the assets. As the case has excited very great interest we offer no apology for giving an outline of the history of the Carter family, and that of the plaintiff, which the evidence has brought to light.

First as to the Carter family. The deceased Bartholomew Carter, who was born about the year 1771, was the second son of Rowland Carter and Sarah Connellan, his wife. The eldest son, named Pat was born about 1766; the marriage of Rowland Carter cannot therefore have taken place later than 1765. The wife of Rowland was a daughter of Bartholomew Connellan of Tubberscanavan, in this county – a man who, as appears by his will, made in 1774, possessed a very considerable landed and chattel property. Rowland died in the last week of 1799, and was at least 34 years married. His wife Sarah Connellan was a Roman Catholic, and differences upon religious matters having taken place between them they separated, when Mrs Carter was in her twentieth year, but they came together again after the death of Bartholomew Connellan. Rowland Carter undoubtedly occupied a highly respectable position in this county – fact which is manifest by his having served as Adjutant in the Independent Volunteers of Tirerill in 1782 and taken a leading part in organising that corps of the patriotic army. For his services on that memorable occasion he was presented with a silver cup, an heirloom which the late doctor highly valued. After his death in 1799 his widow administered, when the chattels were sworn at £500. The freehold property was purchased by the late doctor from his elder brother in 1804 for the sum of £500, both facts show that Rowland was in very independent circumstances at the time of his death. The late doctor having studied in Galway for some time proceeded to Edinburgh in 1791 where he remained until 1796 when he obtained his degree. He then returned to Ballisodare and practised until 1799, in the Autumn of which year he married his cousin Miss Carter, daughter of Captain Carter of Drumlease. The elder brother Pat, proceeded to America after the sale to the doctor, and has not since been heard of. The widow of Rowland died in 1817 and was buried with her husband in the old burying ground of Collooney, where the doctor erected a handsome monument over their remains. At the death of the doctor, the issue of Rowland became extinct, and the next of kin must be sought among other branches.

As the relationship of the defendants Derrig and Devenny, through a sister of Rowlands wife is not disputed, the question arises, is Sir John Benson the first cousin of the deceased.

Before noticing the case which has been successfully relied upon by the plaintiff, it is right to state that in consequence of the connection that exists between the attorney for the defendants and this journal, we feel it would be unbecoming to make any observations on the plaintiffs case, or upon the verdict, which for the present, has declared his right to administration. We shall therefore merely give an outline of his case, in order that the reader may the better understand the detailed report. The case is as follows:

Pat Carter, the father of Rowland Carter, the Volunteer, was married to Ismena Carter, by whom he had two children Rowland and Catherine. Rowland become the father of the deceased doctor and Catherine married a man named Hamilton. After the birth of these children Pat died leaving his widow and them surviving. The period of Pat's death, was according to the Plaintiff's case between 1738 and 1751, and for this reason Mrs Hamilton, Pat's daughter, having died in 1828 aged 90 was born in 1738, and John Benson father of the Plaintiff was born in 1752. If Mrs Benson were previously married to Pat, he must have therefore died within the dates stated. After the death of Pat Carter, his widow Ismena went to service to Cooper's Hill House where, before the year 1762 she contracted a marriage with a fellow servant Thaddeus Benson, the issue of which was John, the father of the plaintiff, born in 1752.

A rest of eight years then took place which was broken in 1760 by the birth of a daughter called Jane, followed in 1761 by the birth of a son Charles, and again in 1762 by the birth of another son Henry. These dates were not given in evidence by the Plaintiff but by the defendants. However, as they are facts which were not questioned, it is better to state them as part of the plaintiffs case. The main points in that case were – the first marriage of Ismena to Pat Carter, the father of Rowland, and her second marriage to Thaddeus Benson, or in other words that the same woman was mother of Rowland Carter and John Benson. To support this case the plaintiff produced the mass of evidence which we give at length, consisting entirely of the reputation of his family, no documentary evidence whatever was given.

On the other hand the defence consisted of evidence intended to raise the presumption that Ismena Benson was not the mother of Rowland Carter, who it was asserted was the child of a former marriage of his father Pat, that by a second marriage Pat had Catherine Carter alias Hamilton, and that the second wife of Pat afterwards became the mother of the Bensons.

For the reasons already stated we refrain from offering any opinion upon either case, feeling that we have sufficiently discharged our duty as journalists by outlining the two sides of the question, and leaving the reader to draw his own conclusion,

We may however state that it is intended to apply on the part of the defendants to set aside the verdict, as against the weight of evidence and the judge's charge."

THE QUACK DOCTOR.

In the *Sligo Chronicle (4/3/1865)* a case was reported concerning Patrick Feeney who was indicted for killing and slaying of Patrick McDonagh at Kilmacowen on the 10th July 1864.

The widow of Patrick McDonagh gave evidence:

"My husband was sick in July last, a day off and a day on. The prisoner was at his house at that time.

I went to the prisoner's house for him. The prisoner came to my husband's house and bled him in the arm. The arm was then tied up but it burst during the night. My husband was well afterwards for three days but he had to go to the Infirmary".

Dr. Little repeated his evidence as to the great swelling of the the arm when he saw it. Although every effort was made to reduce the swelling, mortification ensued and the man died. The mortification was caused by the artery having been severed. An accident of this kind has occurred to qualified surgeons.

To Mr O.Malley (defending) 'I have never severed an artery in bleeding. The deceased was exceedingly weak'. To his Lordship 'The lancet had gone too deep, but there was no want of skill in the binding up. There was want of skill in the vein that was selected.'

Mr. O'Malley then addressed the jury for the prisoner. He contended but for the evidence of Dr. Little there would be no case to go before the Jury, and it was quite clear that throughout the whole of the case the prisoner had acted with a great deal of kindness and charity. All that had been done took place at the solicitation of the deceased's wife; and at any rate there was no doubt the prisoner had acted to the best of his skill and ability. If ever there was a case where a man should get credit for kindness of motive it was this case.

The whole of the evidence was that he bled the man on this occasion, and unfortunately it happened that the artery was near the vein and it was also severed. But Dr. Little had stated that the same accident might occur to a perfectly qualified person. Under the circumstances he did not think it was a case in which a verdict of guilty could be returned.

His Lordship then charged the Jury at considerable length, laying before them all the material facts of the case. There could be no doubt that the prisoner was one of those, unfortunately there were too many, who go about the county treating disease without any professional knowledge.

The Jury then retired to consider their verdict. After a half an hours absence the Jury returned to the court and handed in the following verdict 'Guilty with intent, (sic) and strongly recommend him to mercy'. His Lordship, pronouncing sentence, ordered him to be imprisoned for three months at hard labour.

QUESTION OF SUBMISSION TO DAIL ÉIREANN

The matter arose at a meeting of the Dromore West Board of Guardians(August 7th 1920 *Sligo Independent*). The meeting was to consider the question of granting the doctors an increase in salary, the Board of Guardians having refused to recognise the sealed order of the Local Government issued some time before, fixing the salaries.

Mr Hanley said that they had pledged allegiance to Dáil Éireann as the elected Government of the Irish people, yet the doctor expected that they should submit to the dictation of a foreign Government. The doctors should know that not a single member of that Board would be weak-kneed enough to bend to that Government. Why did not the doctors who derived their living from the Irish people agree to submit their case to the Government these people had elected?

Mr. Clerkin: "Don't they insist on the sealed order of the L.G. Board? They say they are bound hand and foot by it."

Dr. Scott: "We are bound hand and foot by the sealed order. They could leave me out on the road."

Mr. Hanley: "If we are going to ignore the L.G. Board – our officers, as long as they are being paid by us, as representatives of the people, are bound to do the same thing.

It has been said that the L.G. Board would leave Dr. Scott out on the road if he left his case in our hands, but if the L.G. Board wishes let them pay the doctors, but we are not going to pay the doctors for the L.G. Board, unless they obey our orders. It is no good paying the doctors unless we have some little authority over them, and it is about time the doctors should come into line along with us."

Dr. Scott: "It s all very nice, and all very well but it is an old saying 'many men have many minds'. Mr Hanly takes up a certain position, and this Board may take up a certain position but the great question is – have the doctors been treated properly for the years past? I have been here for 44 $^1/_2$ years, and I assure your if I was a man making money I could turn around and retire, and I wish to God I could. I never made only barely what fed me, and put clothes on me since I came into the Union. Men will say– 'you are rolling in money' but I say it is a down right falsehood. If I was sufficiently paid I would no more ask this board for an increase in salary that I would stand on my head."

Mr Hanley: I won't for the present go into whether you are well treated, or badly treated, but until such times as the doctors are satisfied to place themselves unreservedly in our hands, and take themselves out of the hands of the L.G. Board, I will never consent to have anything whatsoever to do with them."

Rec[...] with thanks.
[...]
[...]ird
November 12. 1902.

Wine St . Sligo.
1st August 1902

The Representatives
of the late L. W. Hunter Esq.
To Doctor Laird for
Professional Attendance :

£50·0·0.

Over.

9 visits in town.
68 Special visits at
Washington.
5 nights in Washington.
Medicines supplied.

Appendix: List of Sligo Doctors.

SLIGO 1780 [Watson's Almanac]
CORONERS FOR SLIGO

W. O'BEIRNE – Drumcliffe

HENRY IRWIN – Moy Deagh

SLIGO 1785 – 1820

The treble Almanac – incorporating Wilson's Dublin Directory, Watson's Irish Almanac, and Exshaws English Court Registry 1787 – 1837 (The Mercer Library)

CHARLES OVENDEN L.R.C.S.I. 1801-1809

CHARLES OVENDEN – 1778 – 1811 Surgeon, Sligo and Fermanagh. 'Eighteenth Century Medics': P.J. and R.V. Wallis, New Castle on Tyne 1988.

WILLIAM BELL L.R.C.S.I – Sligo 1809 –1820.

JOHN THOMAS FERGUSON L.R.C.S.I. Sligo 1815-1817.

PET ORMSBY L.R.C.S.I., Sligo *Staff – Sligo Infirmary 1815 - 1819*

WILLIAM ARMSTRONG L.R.C.S.I Sligo 1818-1820.

The above list is the total number of Sligo doctors recorded in almanacs from 1785 - 1820. There was no mention of Dr. Todd.

SLIGO 1820: APOTHECARIES AND SURGEONS
[COMMERCIAL DIRECTORY]

ANDERSON, FRANCIS (Surgeon), Radcliffe St. (or Ratciffe St.)

ARMSTRONG, WM. (Surgeon), Knox's St.

BELL, WILLIAM (Surgeon), Stephen St.

BURNE, JOHN (Surgeon), Market St.

MCMUNN, SAMUEL, Market St.

MC NAIER, JAMES (Surgeon), Castle St.

MURRAY, JOHN, Stephen St.,

PHYSICIANS

BOLTON, R. Knox's St
CARTER, BARTHOLOMEW, Wine St.
COYLE, BERNARD, Knox's St.
IRWIN, HENRY, Stephen St.
JACKSON R.D., Market St.
JOHNSON CHARLES, Stephen St.,

SLIGO 1824 [PIGOT & CO. DIRECTORY]

ARMSTRONG, WM. Knox's St.
BELL, WILLIAM [County Surgeon] Stephen St.

PHYSICIANS

BLACKMAN, JERVIS, WINE ST.
CARTER, BARTHOLOMEW, W ine St.
COYLE, BERNARD, Knox's St.
IRWIN, HENRY, Stephen St. (Surgeon to the Sligo Militia and Inspector of Hospitals)
KENNY, JAMES, Correction St.

APOTHECARIES

ANDERSON, FRANCIS (and Surgeon) Ratcliff St.
ARMSTRONG, WILLIAM, Knox's St.
BURNE, JOHN (and Surgeon), High St.
MCMUNN, Samuel, Market St.
MURRAY, JOHN, Stephen St.

According to Pigot's Directory: In that year the Sligo Mail Coach left Sligo every morning at half past nine, going through Boyle, Drumsna, Longford, Rathowen and Mullingar. It went on to Kinnegad where it met The Galway Mail on its way to Dublin. The Sligo Mail Coach returned by the same route to Sligo every afternoon at twenty minutes past four!

SLIGO DIRECTORY 1837
PHYSICIANS

ARMSTRONG, ARCHIBALD, 31 Knox's St.
BURROWS, THOMAS M.D, Riverside
CARTER, BARTHOLOMEW, 30 Wine St. Surgeon to the Jail.

DEVITT, MICHAEL, 7 John St.
HENRY, ALEXANDER 13 Chapel Lane.
HOMAN, TRAVERS, 8 Wine St.
HUME, ANDREW, 46 The Mall.
KENNY, JAMES 56 Correction St.
KNOTT, EDWARD, 19 Wine St.
LITTLE, THOMAS, 13 Correction St.
LYNN, ROBERT, 20Knox's St.
McMUNN, JOHN 3 Ratcliff St.

SLIGO DIRECTORY 1839

PHYSICIANS – AS FOR 1837

COUNTY INFIRMARY (1839)

Physician –	THOMAS LITTLE. M.D.
Treasurer –	R.B. WYNNE ESQ.
House Steward –	MR JOHN GILLIS.
Matron –	M.GILLIS.

SLIGO FEVER HOSPITAL

Physicians:	TRAVERS HOMAN M.D; EDWARD KNOTT M.D.
Apothecary:	MR. HENRY EBLING.
Treasurer: Rev.	WILLIAM ARMSTRONG.
House Steward:	MR. JOHN MORRIS.
Matron:	M.DOOLAN.

SLIGO DISPENSARY

Physicians:	ROBERT LYNN M.D. and THOMAS BURROWS M.D.
Apothecary::	MR HENRY EBLIN.
House Steward:	MR WILLIAM WHELAN.

ST. JOHN'S DISPENSARY

Physicians –	JAMES KENNY M.D. and THOMAS ARMSTRONG M.D
Apothecary:	MR. R. H. WOOD.
House Steward:	MR SAMUEL MULHOLLAND.

IRISH MEDICAL DIRECTORY 1843

This was the first Medical Directory in Ireland. By Henry Croly;

SLIGO COUNTY
POPULATION 171,765

Ballymote
LOUGHEED, JOSEPH, M.D. (EDINB) (sometimes Longheed), M.R.C.S.L., Lic Apoth. Medical Attendant of Dispensary, Constabulary and Revenue Police.

Ballysadere (Ballisadare)
SIMPSON, ADAM, Late Surgeon Royal Navy.

Carney
HAMILTON, WILLIAM RICHARD MD (Edin) L.R.C.S.E Medical Attendant of Dispensary and Constabulary.

Collooney:
ARMSTRONG, THOMAS. M.D. (EDINB) LRCSE. Medical Attendant of Collooney Dispensary & Constabulary and St. John's Dispensary, Sligo.

Cliffoney:
TUTHILL, Medical Attendant of Dispensary and Constabulary.

Coolaney:
KELLY, SAMUEL LRCSI, Medical Attendant of Dispensary and Constabulary.
EASKEY: McMUNN, JAMES. Lic Apoth.

Riverstown:
LOUGHEED, JOSEPH, Lic. Apoth; TIGHE, DOMINICK. Apoth.

Tubbercurry:
MEEKNESS, JOHN FREDERICK, M.D. M.R.C.S.L. Acc Dubl. L.H. Medical Attendant of Dispensary & Constabulary;
DURKIN THOMAS, Apothecary.

SLIGO TOWN 1843
POPULATION 15,152

ARMSTRONG, ARCHIBALD, 31 Knox's St. M.D Lic Apoth. Acc. Dublin L.H

BURROWS, THOMAS M.D, (EDIN) Medical Attendant of Sligo and Riverstown Dispensaries & Riverstown Constabulary;

CARTER, BARTHOLOMEW, 30 Wine St. Surgeon to the Jail.

CONNELAN, PETER, Late of R.N.

DEVITT, MICHAEL, Stephen St. M.R.C.S.L. Late Army Surgeon. Acc. Dbl. L.H.

HOMAN, TRAVERS, 8 Wine St. M.D, (EDIN) M.R.C.S.L. Medical Attendant of Sligo Fever Hospital; Dispensary & Constabulary & Dromore West Dispensary.

HUME, ANDREW, 46 The Mall. M.D, (EDIN) Acc. Edinburgh L.H. L.R.C.S.I. Medical Attendant of Constabulary.

JOHNSTON, JOHN JAMES, (Castle St.) M.R.C.S.L. Lic Apoth.

KENNY, JAMES, Mass Lane. Medical Attendant Sligo Dispensary

KNOTT, EDWARD, Castle St.M.D, (EDIN),L.R.C.S.I. Medical Attendant of Fever Hospital and Union Workhouse.

LITTLE, THOMAS, Jail St. M.D. L.L.D. L.R.C.S.I. Surgeon to County Infirmary.

LYNN, ROBERT, Wine St., A.B. M.B. T.C.D.. ACC. DUBL. L.H. Medical Attendant of Sligo Dispensary.

McMUNN, JOHN 3 Ratcliffe St. Lic Apoth.

TUCKER, WILLIAM JAMES/Radcliffe St. M.D. M.R.C.S.L.; Lic. Apoth. Acc. Dubl. L/H. Medical Attendant of St. John's Dispensary

VERNON, JAMES DALY. M.R.C.S.L.

LOUGHEED, JOHN (Market St.) Lic. Apoth.

ROGERS – Lic. Apoth. (Conducting Murrays Establishment).

WOOD, RICHARD (Radcliffe St.) Lic. Apoth.

During the fearful visitation of Asiatic Cholera in 1832 several Medical Practioners of Sligo, and also Dr. Leahy, King's Professor of Medicine, who had gone to Sligo to investigate the disease were "successively cut off by that malady".

THE IRISH MEDICAL DIRECTORY 1846
SLIGO COUNTY (HENRY CROLY)

Ballymote
LOUGHEED, JOSEPH, M.D. M.R.C.S (Eng. '16) (sometimes Longheed), Lic Apoth. Medical Attendant of Dispensary, Constabulary and Revenue Police & Post Master.
MOTHERWELL, JAMES B. L.R.C.S.I.

Ballysadere (Ballisadare)
SIMPSON, ADAM, Late Surgeon Royal Navy '25.

Carney,
HAMILTON, William Richard MD (Edin'27)   L.R.C.S Medical Attendant of Dispensary and Constabulary.

Cliffoney:
TUTHILL, MICHAEL. Med. Att. of Disp & Constab.

Collooney:
ARMSTRONG, THOMAS. M.D. (EDINB) LRCSE. Medical Attendant of Collooney Dispensary & Constabulary and St. John's Dispensary, Sligo.

Coolaney:
KELLY, SAMUEL LRCSI, Medical Attendant of Dispensary and Constabulary.

Easkey: McMUNN, JAMES. Lic Apoth.

Iceford: CUSTIS, James L.R.C.S.I.

Riverstown:
LOUGHEED, JOSEPH, Lic. Apoth;
TIGHE, DOMINICK. Apoth.

Tubbercurry:
MEEKINGS, JOHN FREDERICK, M.D. M.R.C.S. (Eng. '33) F.R.C.S.I '44. Acc Dubl. L.H. Medical Attendant of Dispensary & Constabulary;
DURKIN THOMAS, Apothecary.

TOWN OF SLIGO

ARMSTRONG, ARCHIBALD, 31 Knox's St. M.D Lic Apoth. Acc. Dublin (Lying -in-H)

BURROWS, THOMAS M.D, (EDIN '26) Medical Attendant of Sligo and Riverstown Dispensaries & Riverstown Constabulary;

CARTER, BARTHOLOMEW, M.D. (EDIN) 30 Wine St. Physician to the Jail.

CHAMBERS, JAMES W. MD. LRCSI

CONNELAN, PETER, Late of R.N.

DEVITT, MICHAEL, Stephen St. M.R.C.S.L. Late Army Surgeon. Acc. Dbl. L.H.

HOMAN, TRAVERS, 8 Wine St. M.D, (EDIN '27), M.R.C.S. (Eng'28) F.R.C.S.I. ('44) Medical Attendant of Sligo Fever Hospital; Dispensary & Constabulary & Dromore West Dispensary.

HUME, ANDREW, 46 The Mall. M.D, (EDIN '30) Acc. Edinburgh L.H. L.R.C.S.I. Medical Attendant of Constabulary.

JOHNSTON, JOHN JAMES, (Castle St.) M.R.C.S. (Eng.) Lic Apoth.

KELLY, SAMUEL L.R.C.S.I

KENNY, JAMES, Mass Lane. Medical Attendant Sligo Dispensary

KNOTT, EDWARD, Castle St.M.D, (EDIN '30), Fellow and L.R.C.S.I. Medical Attendant of Fever Hospital and Union Workhouse.

LITTLE, THOMAS, Jail St. M.D. L.L.D. F and L.R.C.S.I. Surgeon to County Infirmary.

LOUGHEED, JOHN. Market St. Lic Apoth.

LYNN, ROBERT KERRISON , Wine St., A.B. M.B. Fellow and L.R.C.S.I. Acc Dubl. L.H. Medical Attendant of Sligo Dispensary and Medical Ref. of Standard Life Assurance Company.

McMUNN, JOHN M.D. 3 Ratcliffe St. Lic Apoth.

PATTERSON, EDWARD G.L. R.C.S.I.

TUCKER, WILLIAM JAMES/Radcliffe St. M.D. M.R.C.S. (Eng); Lic. Apoth. Acc. Dubl. L/H. Medical Attendant of St. John's Dispensary. Member of Town Council.

VERNON, JAMES DALY. M.R.C.S. (Eng. '37)

O'ROURKE, FRANCIS, Lic Apoth.

ROGERS – Lic. Apoth.

WOOD, RICHARD (Radcliffe St.) Lic. Apoth.

LOUGHEED, JOHN, Market St.. Lic. Apoth.

MEDICAL DIRECTORY FOR IRELAND 1852

Sligo County Infirmary:
Established 1765. *Number of beds* –80; *Physician and Surgeon* W.S. Little M.B; *House Surgeon:* Mr T. Dolan; *Apothecary:* Mr J. Johnstone; *Secretary:* R.B. Wynne Esq.; *Matron:* Miss Gillas; *Average Number of In Patients:* 820 per annum; *Out Patients:* 1100 per annum.

County Fever Hospital:
Established 1822. *Number of beds* –122; *Physician and Surgeon* T. Homan M.D. and E. Knott M.D; *Apothecary:* Mr C.J. Denning; *Secretary: & Treasurer* Captain Knox.; *Matron:* Mrs Morris; *Average Number of Patients:* 512 per annum;

DISPENSARIES

Ahamlish
Established 1840. *Medical Officer:* J. Powell; *Secretary: & Treasurer* E. Smith Esq..; *Average Number of Patients:* 40–50 per diem;

Ballymote:
Established 1818. *Medical Officer:* J. Lougheed M.D; *Secretary::* Rev. J. Garrett. ; *Average Number of Patients:* 1800 per annum.

Carney:
Established 1834. *Physician and Surgeon*: W. R. Hamilton M.D; Apothecary: Mr. T. McCoy *Secretary::* Rev. J. Jeffcott ;

Castleconnor:
Established 1825. *Physician and Surgeon*: W. Whittaker M.D; Apothecary: Mr. R. Atkinson; *Secretary::* Rev. S. Stock ; *Average Number of Patients:* about 2000 per annum.

Tubbercurry:
Established 1833. *Medical Officer:* T.D. Vernon M.D; *Secretary::* Rev. J. Hamilton; *Average Number of Patients:* about 100 per week.

MEDICAL DIRECTORY FOR IRELAND 1854
IRISH UNIONS CO. SLIGO

NAME OF UNION DISTRICT		POPULATION	EXT IN ACRES	AVERAGE NO PATIENTS	MEDICAL OFFICER	SALARY
DROMORE	EASKEY	8,896	4,2291	796	J.McMUNN	£60
WEST	SKREEN	6,613	3,2734	2,160	R. McMUNN	£70
UNION	C...CONNOR	4,054	2,1960	—	R.McMUNN	£60
T. CURRY	TUBBER..	18,358	8,2633	—	J.D. VERNON	£100
UNION	COOLANEY	7,723	4,3139	—	SAMUEL KELLY	£100
SLIGO	CARNEY	13,833	44,554	JOHN POWELL& WM HAMILTON		£200
UNION	SLIGO	239,929	30,385	—	DR. McMUNN	£190
	COLLOONEY	7,473	25,443	2,850	W. ARMSTRONG	£100
	BALLYMOTE	6,386	19,138	60	J. LONGHEED	£100
	RIVERSTOWN	6,944	23,551	—	DR. T. BURROWS	£100

MEDICAL DIRECTORY FOR IRELAND 1862

SLIGO TOWN

ARMSTRONG, A,	1837	Stephen St. Aphoth. Sligo Gaol.
DENNING, J	1845	22, Knox St.
FAWCETT R.	1854	Thornhill Hse. Asst. Sur. Sligo Militia
HOMAN, TRAVERS,	1827	8 Wine St. F.R.C.S.I.
FAWCETT, J.	1840	51, John's St. He had strong military pull.
JOHNSTON J.J.	1832	Castle St. Apoth. Co. Inf.
LITTLE, W.S.	1835	Wrote in Journals on Cholera, Anasthetic Abuse, Brain Trauma, Tetanus.
LYNN, R.K,	1830	Stephen St. F.R.C.S Physician to Jail.
TUCKER, J.	1836	M.D. Glasgow. He wrote on Cholera, Use of Iron Iodide. The Reformed Roman Thermo-Electrical bath.

COUNTY SLIGO 1862

Ballymote: LOUGHEED J. 1816.; MCMUNN; POWELL 1827.
Cliffoney: HOZIER W.H. 1856
Collooney: ARMSTRONG W. 1858.
Tubbercurry: CONOLON, P. 1827; McCARTHY, J. 1855;
VERNON, J.P. 1837.

SLATERS DIRECTORY 1880
PHYSICIANS AND SURGEONS SLIGO TOWN

COX, ML.	Wine St.
DENNING, FRANCIS A.	22, Knox St. & 13 Castle St.
LAIRD, JOHN M.D.,	Quay St.
MacDOWEL, EFFINGHAM. M.D.	The Mall.
LITTLE, W.S.	Albert St.
MURRAY, THOMAS M.D.	Stephen St.,
PALMER, THOMAS M.D.	Stephen St.
WHITE, P.M.	19 Castle St.
WOOD, RD. H. M.D	Wine St.

DIRECTORY OF SLIGO FOR 1881
PHYSICIANS AND SURGEONS SLIGO TOWN

COX, ML.	Wine St.
DENNING, FRANCIS A.	22, Knox St. & Castle St.
LAIRD, JOHN M.D.,	Quay St.
MacDOWEL, EFFINGHAM. M.D.	The Mall.
MURRAY, THOMAS M.D.	Stephen St.,
PALMER, THOMAS M.D.	Stephen St.
WHITE, P.M.	19 Castle St.
WOOD, RD. H. M.D	Wine St.

DIRECTORY OF COUNTY SLIGO FOR 1889
MEDICAL GENTLEMEN SLIGO TOWN

DENNING, FRANCIS A.	The Mall
LAIRD, JOHN M.D.,	Wine St.
MARTYN, R.F.	Stephen St.
MURRAY, THOMAS M.D.	The Mall.
MacDOWEL, EFFINGHAM. M.D.	The Mall.
PALMER, THOMAS M.D.	Stephen St.

THE SLIGO INDEPENDENT COUNTY DIRECTORY
ALMANAC AND GUIDE 1889

Ballymote Dispensary:
Established 1818. *Medical Officer:* Dr. McMunn M.D;

Cliffoney Dispensary:
Med.Officer: Dr. John Tate.

Coolaney Dispensary:
Medical Officer: Dr. Hunt (Open every Wednesday and Saturday)

Collooney Dispensary:
Medical Officer: Dr. Lucas; *Coroner:* Dr. Roe.
Open every Monday and Thursday

Carney Dispensary
Established 1834. *MedicalOfficer*: Dr. Roe.

Tubbercurry Dispensary:
Established 1833. *Medical Officer:* Dr. Flannery.

Riverstown Dispensary:
Medical Officer : Dr. A. Frazer (Open Monday and Thursday)

MEDICAL DIRECTORY 1897
SLIGO TOWN

E. CORBETT (Surgeon Dentist); F.A.V. DENNING: A.J. EADES; T. GILCHRIST; J. LAIRD (Disp); W. J. LOUGHEED; D. MAGUIRE; E.C. MacDOWEL (Inf); R.J. MARTYN (Disp); T.S. MURRAY (Workhouse); J.J.O'DONNELL; J. PETIT (Asylum).

SLIGO 1897

Name of Union & Dispensary District		Medical Officer	Salary of Medical Officers	Vaccination Fees To Medical Officers
DROMORE	EASKEY	A.J.McMUNN	£100	£92
WEST		H.M. SCOTT	£100	£92
UNION	SKREEN	J.J.McNULTY	£100	£17
T..CURRY	ACLARE	JAS. GUNNING	£100	£32
UNION	COOLANEY	A.M. HUNT	£100	£47
	TUBBER..	JAMES G. FLANNERY	£100	£16

KILGANNONS ALMANAC AND DIRECTORY 1907
SLIGO TOWN

Medical Gentlemen

DENNING	Knox's St.
MARTYN, R. J.	Stephen St.
MacDOWEL, E.C.	The Mall
LAIRD, JOHN,	Wine St.
QUINN. P.M.	Quay St.

MEDICAL DIRECTORY 1910 COUNTY SLIGO

Bunnanaden:	J.L. PHIBBS	Gurteen:	M.A. BOYLE
Banada:	J. GUNNING		
Easkey:	D.F.R. CLARKE, F.G. FENTON		
Cliffoney:	T. GIBBONS	Coolaney: A. M HUNT	
Dromard:	P.O'HART		
Enniscrone:	W.I.CONNELL; T. ROUSE; H.M. SCOTT.		
Riverstown:	E.K. FRAZER; HARRIET McCLOGHRY.		
Tubbercurry:	JAS. G. FLANNERY; JOHN A. FLANNERY.		
Skreen :	J. J. MCNULTY; Templeboy:	D. MAGUIRE.	

SLIGO TOWN 1910
(POP. 10,870)

F.A. Denning; P.J. Flanagan; J. Laird; T. Gilchrist; J.J. Kerr; A.H. Laird; J. W. Lougheed; E.C. MacDowel; R.J. Martyn; J. Petit; P.M. Quinn; R. G. Roe.

CO. SLIGO GUIDE 1912

As above for Sligo Town.

MEDICAL DIRECTORY 1930:
SLIGO COUNTY

Achonry:	F.J.N.CARNEY
Ballintogher:	E. MORAN, KATHLEEN MORAN.
BALLYMOTE:	T.J. GILMARTIN; J.P. KILFEATHER;
	J.J. MacANDREWS; T.W. McDONAGH;
	T.F. O'CARROLL.
Bunnanaden:	ANNE M. O'DOWD
Charlesfoot:	S.A. CLARKE.

Cashelgarron: M.J.A. MARTIN; P.O'HART
Cliffoney: J.CLANCY; T. McGOWAN.
Collooney: E.T.CUMMINGS; HONORA J. DOYLE; E.S. FOLEY;
Easkey: D.F.R. CLARKE; M.J.KEVANY
Enniscrone: P.J. CLARKE; R.F. GORDON.
Gurteen: T.D. DONEGAN;
Riverstown: WINIFRED M.O'HANLON
Templeboy: M.J. HARTE;   Tourlestrane: T.F. ARMSTRONG.
Tubbercurry: MARGARET M. ARMSTRONG; M. BRENNAN;
V.P. DONOHUE; EVELINE M. FLANNERY;
JOHN A. J. FLANNERY A.J. GALLAGHER.

SLIGO TOWN 1930 (POP. 10,870)

Henrietta Broderick; P.J. Burke; E.V. Connolly; Olive M.Fair;
Bridget M.Foley; T. Gilcrest; J.J. Kerr; C.J.McCarthy; H.P.
McLaughlin; J.P Moran; G.J.J. O'Donnell; P.M. Quinn; T.H. Quinn;
T. Rouse; B. F. Shea; H.J. Swan; Marcella B. M. Swan; Annette K.
Woodmartin.

SLIGO TRADES DIRECTORY – 1936 SLIGO TOWN

BURKE, P.J.   Cloonamahon Sanitorium, Tuberculosis Officer.
McCARTHY, C.J.   The Mall, Surgeon County Infirmary.
McCREADY, G.   The Mall.
McLAUGHLIN, H.   The Mall, County Infirmary.
Fever Hospital.
MORAN, J.P.   Stephen St., Coroner.
O'DONNELL, G.   Imperial Hotel.
QUINN, J.S.M.B.   Wine St.
QUINN, P.M.   Albert Rd.
ROUSE, THOMAS M.D. Wine St.
SWAN, H.J.   Weston House.

MEDICAL DIRECTORY, 1945 SLIGO

Ballisadare: J.F MARTIN; B.D. CRICHTON;
Ballymote: J.J. B. CONNOLLY; E.S. McDONAGH;
M. DONAGH; P.O'HART
Cashelgarron: M.J.A. MARTIN; Cliffoney: P. HERAUGHTY.

Collooney: A. T. GALLAGHER; CHRISTINA J. GALLAGHER;
Coolaney: T.W. MCDONAGH
Dromore West: KATHLEEN M.CONNOLLY.
Easkey: D.M CLARKE; OLIVIA M.J. CLARKE;
               R.R. J.R. CLARKE; W. J. MCGUIRE.
Enniscrone: C.S. O'CONNOR; J.E. ADAMSON.
Geevagh: M.P. DELANEY;
Riverstown: M.F. BECKETT; J.P. KILFEATHER.
Skreen: M.J. HARTE   Tourlestrane: M. BRENNAN
Tubbercurry: EVELINE M. FLANNERY; A. J. FLANNERY .

SLIGO TOWN 1945 (POP. 11,437)

P.J. Burke; C.J.McCarthy; T.J. Murphy; Brigid Corrigan; A.P. McLaughlin; G.J.J. O'Donnell; J. P. Dodd; Theresa Cunningham; S. G. Mecredy; T.H. Quinn; J. P. Moran; D.S. Reid; M.B. Flanagan; P. J. Mullin; B. F. Shea; J. F. Keenan; M. Kirby; Nora Murphy;

Omitted: J.P. Perceval, The Mall; Timothy Foley, James Clyne, Sheila Henry, Mental Hospital.

COUNTY SLIGO ANNUAL REPORT FOR 1945

Aclare: DR. M. BRENNAN.
Ballymote: DR. P.O'HART.
Carney: DR. M.J. MARTIN.
Cliffoney: DR. E. CONNOLLY-FLANAGAN.
Coolaney: DR. T. MCDONAGH.
Easkey No1:   DR. T. ARMSTRONG.
Easkey No. 2: DR. C.S. O'CONNOR
Geevagh: DR. H. MCDONAGH
Gurteen: DR. P. J. KILCOYNE
Riverstown: DR. J. P. KILFEATHER.
Skreen: DR. M.J. HARTE;
Tubbercurry: DR. J.A. FLANNERY

SLIGO TOWN 1965

MURPHY, THOMAS .   Weston House
HERAUGHTY, PATRICK.   The Mall. He as now retired to
Dublin and his Practice is being continued by his son Domhnall.
TWOMEY, EMILY.   The Mall.
DORMAN, MICHAEL.   The Mall.
HENRY, PATRICK J.   Stephen St.
O'CONNOR, MICHAEL   Wine St.
EGAN, FRANK   Teeling St.
SWAN, THURLOC,   Surgeon, Sligo General Hosp..
COLLINS, DERMOT M.   Physician, Sligo General Hosp..
DONOVAN, WILLIAM.   Gynaecologist/Obs. Sligo General.
FOX, JOHN.   Radiologist, Sligo General.
TWOMEY, JEREMIAH.   Anaesthetist, Sligo General.
BOLAND, DENIS.   Surgeon, Wine St.
POWER, PATRICK.   Assistant Medical Officer of Health.
FOLEY, TIMOTHY.   Sligo Mental Hospital.
KLYNE, JAMES.   Sligo Mental Hospital.
DONOVAN, MARIE.   The Mall.
DEVINS, SHEILA.   Sligo Mental Hospital.
QUINN, THOMAS.   Ophthalmologist, Wine St.
MAHON, DESMOND.   Ophthalmologist, The Mall,

SLIGO COUNTY

Ballymote: FRANK O'HART; THOMAS TAHENY.
Cliffoney: EVELYN FLANAGAN.
Coolaney: T.W. MCDONAGH
Carney: MICHAEL MARTIN.
Easkey No1:   THOMAS ARMSTRONG.
Easkey No 2: CHRISTY O'CONNOR.
Geevagh: JIM CLANCY.
Grange: FRANK MAGUIRE.
Riverstown: J.P. KILFEATHER.
Tubbercurry: SEAN FLANNERY; JOHN A. FLANNERY;
                  JOE CULLEN; TONY KIRRANE;

REGISTRARS OF BIRTHS, DEATHS AND MARRIAGES
(CO.SLIGO)

Sligo No. 1 Dispensary.

1864-1866	ROBERT LYNN.
1866- 1875	JAMES TUCKER.
1875-1912	JOHN LAIRD; ARTHUR DENNING.
1913-1940	JOHN ROUSE.
1941-1967	T.J. MURPHY
1968-1970'S	BRIAN GALLAGHER.

Sligo No. 2 Dispensary.

1864- 1875	JAMES TUCKER; HENRY K. VISCON; ARTHUR DENNING; T.D. FALMER;
1885-1923	P.N. WHITE.
1923-1959	J.P. MORAN.
1960-1980	P. HERAUGHTY.

Sligo No. 3 Dispensary.

1952- 1970's	ML. O'CONNOR.

Aclare.

1866	P.F. MCGLOIN.
1906- 1909	JAS. GUNNING; JOHN A. FLANNERY.
1933-1954	DR. MARTIN BRENNAN.
1954-1956	DR. A. KIRRANE.
1956-1965	DR. M.A. O'TOOLE.
1965 - 1980	DR. L. GAVAGHAN.

Skreen.

1864-1880	ROBERT McMUNN.
1880-1884	DANIEL MAGUIRE.
1884-1887	GEO. F. ROUGHAN.
1887-1912	J.J. MCNULTY.
1912-1922	W.J. COWELL.
1926-1957	MARTIN J. HARTE.
1958-1966	W. JUDGE.
1966- 1968	ROSE JUDGE.

Easkey

1864-1874	JAMES MCMUNN.
1874-1875	THOMAS H. SCOTT.
1876-1892	CHAS MAHON.
1892-1902	J.McMUNN.

1904-1930	D.F. CLARKE.
1930	T. FEENEY.
1937-1960'S	T. F. ARMSTRONG.
1967-1971	W.MCGUIRE.

Enniscrone

1864-1875	JAMES J. NOLAN
1876-1925	H.M.SCOTT.
1925-1936	P.J.CLARKE
1936-1937	P.COWELL
1937-1977	C.S. O'CONNOR.

Gurteen

1865-1867	T.D. PALMER.
1900-1919	M.A. BOYLE.
1920-1922	D.J. DOYLE.
1924-1931	A.T. GALLAGHER (Collooney)
1932- 1966	P.J. KILCOYNE.

Riverstown

1864-1873	THOMAS BURROWS.
1873-1879	J.W.SHAW.
1879-1888	WM ROSS.
1888-1918	E. FRAZER.
1919-1964	T.P. KILFEATHER.

Carney No. 2 (Cliffoney)

1864-1871	EVORY CHARMICHAEL.
1871-1875	T. POPHAM.
1875-1878	R. G. ROE (Coolaney).
1878-1880	L.I. O'NEILL.
1881-1890	JOHN W.TATE (Lay Registrars in Interval).
1934-1936	C.S. O'CONNOR (Enniscrone).
1937-1970'S	DR. EVELYN FLANAGAN.

Collooney

1865-1875	W. ARMSTRONG, AYRES MOORE.
1878-1884	JOHN MOLONY.
1885-1890	WM HAMILTON; WM. C. LUCAS.
1890-1926	E.T. CUMMINGS.
1926-1931	EAMON MCSEARRAIG.
1932-1966	A.T. GALLAGHER.
1966.	STANLEY HARTE.

Coolaney

1846-1878	ROWLAND BLENNER HASSETT.
1878-1885	R.G. ROE (FROM CLIFFONEY).
1885-1943	OWEN GANNON.
1943-1975	T.W. McDONAGH.

Carney No. 1 (Cashelgarron)

1864-1875	WM. R. HAMILTON.
1878-1898	ROBERT G. ROE. (lay Registrar followed).
1926	DR. M. MARTIN.
1960'S	DR. FRANK MAGUIRE.

Geevagh

1864	JOHN C. FRY
1864-1879	W, FRAZER.
1879-1881	W.J. KISBY.
1881-1892	CHARLES D.B. BARRETT; BERNARD CONLON.
1899-1904	JOHN McMENAMON.
1904-1908	THOM. MORAN (Lay Registrars followed).
1945	DR. H. McDONAGH.
1946/7	DR. P.O'BERINE
1949	DR. J. CLANCY.

Ballymote

1864-1868	S. McMUNN.
1868-1898	ANDREW McMUNN.
1898-1899	JOHN A. McMUNN
1901-1911	J. GILMARTIN.
1911-1912	P.O'HART.
1913-1928	ML. DOYLE. (Lay Registrars followed).
LATER	DR. P. O'HART; DR. F. O'HART.

Tubbercurry

1864-1865	JOSEPH MCCARTHY.
1866-1873	THOMAS STANLEY MURRAY.
1874-1876	ML. WHITE.
1877	D. CLEMENTS MASSEY; WM WEST.
1878	JAMES G. FLANNERY.
1930	JOHN A. FLANNERY;
LATER	SEAN FLANNERY.

THE AUTHOR

PATRICK JAMES HENRY was born in Sligo in 1928.

He received his early education in Sligo and later at Blackrock College Dublin.

He qualified as a Doctor at the Royal College of Surgeons in 1953. Having spent several years in England he returned to work in General Practice in Sligo.

He was President of the Irish College of General Practitioners in 1988.

He married Mary Gilheany in 1956 and they have two daughters and one son.